Statistical Mapping
and the Presentation of Statistics

BY

G. C. DICKINSON

Lecturer in Geography, University of Leeds

EDWARD ARNOLD (PUBLISHERS) LTD

First published 1963
Reprinted 1964
Reprinted 1967
Reprinted 1968

SBN 7131 5117 X

GA
109
.8
.D5

Printed in Great Britain by
The Camelot Press Ltd., London and Southampton

STATISTICAL MAPPING
AND THE PRESENTATION OF STATISTICS

TO
MY WIFE

Contents

Acknowledgements

THE AUTHOR wishes to express his thanks to Mr. P. Shrives and Mr. G. Bryant for their assistance with the illustrations in this book and to the Editors of *The Town Planning Review* for permission to use Fig. 2 from Vol. XXXIII, No. 1 (April 1962); to the Research Paper Series, Department of Geography, the University of Chicago for Fig. X-8 from G. F. White (ed.), *Papers on Flood Problems* (copyright by the University of Chicago); to *The Guardian* for a graph from the edition of 6th June 1961; to W. and A. K. Johnston and G. W. Bacon Ltd. for permission to use part of p. 13 of Bacon, *All Essentials School Atlas*; to the Army Map Service, Washington, for the figure on p. 23 of *A.M.S. Bulletin*, No. 11, September 1944; to the *Evening News* for permission to reproduce two posters; and to the Controller of H.M. Stationery Office for permission to reproduce the list of Census Reports (contained in the Appendix) from *Guides to Official Sources No. 2*.

Introduction

IT WAS in 1753 that Mr. Thornton, Member of Parliament for the City of York, opposed a Bill proposing to establish a national census for Great Britain by declaring that he did not believe 'that there was any set of men, or, indeed, any individual of the human species so presumptuous and so abandoned as to make the proposal we have just heard. . . . I hold this project to be totally subversive of the last remnants of English liberty . . . the new Bill will direct the imposition of new taxes, and, indeed, the addition of a very few words will make it the most effectual engine of rapacity and oppression that was ever used against an injured people.'

One cannot help wondering whether the citizens of York should not have been congratulated on the unusual perspicacity of their Member, for he and his fellow supporters (they were successful for a time) were, of course, attempting to stem not merely a single new Bill in Parliament but something of much greater importance—the onset of a new era of government. Today, for better or worse, we live in that era which is among other things an age of measurement and statistics. We count, measure and calculate about all aspects of life in a manner which even Mr. Thornton could scarcely have foreseen and our modern 'experts' are no longer revered personages drawing on long acquaintance in a particular field or working by intuition and 'experience', but men who can adapt and use this calculating most successfully to promote their own activities and predict the future.

Parallel with this pervasion of statistics into everyday life has come the need to acquaint an ever-increasing number of people with their implications. Governments are perhaps the most prolific 'counters' of all, and since official statistics can be a two-edged weapon it becomes important to ensure that the electorate understands both the nature and implications of such statistics relating to Government activity as may come to their notice. Growing awareness of the importance of public relations has led industry to follow a similar line, supplementing its long history of private calculating by placing before the public eye those facts and figures which it considers of interest or advertisement value; in fields such as Town and Country Planning it becomes essential to use all manner of statistics to summarise the present and predict future trends.

On all sides and through a wide variety of media we are constantly assailed by statistics —how our Taxes or Rates are spent, how many houses are needed, have been or will be built, how many more cars, or television sets or tins of meat or jam-jars made by Bloggs & Co. are used in preference to those made by their competitors, and so on; since it has long been recognised that 'dry' statistics are made both more intelligible and more interesting by pictorial or semi-pictorial representation there has also been considerably increased interest in the techniques available for this purpose. In many cases today where statistics are presented publicly it is the man in the street, the very general observer, whose attention is being sought and who is now taking his place alongside older-established, more specialised assessors of statistical material. In many fields of study, such as Geography, Economics and Social Studies it has long been impossible to present a complete picture without recourse to statistics and an understanding of them, and above all a knowledge of the techniques available for passing on to other people an idea of their implications, has always formed a fundamental requirement of teaching and research in those subjects.

It is to all those faced with this problem of presenting statistical information to a wider public that this book is addressed, and particularly to those who are encountering this problem for the first time, whether in the formulation of a thesis or piece of research, as part of a carefully organised publicity campaign or simply as a formal teaching requirement in a standard course of cartography at school or university. Essentially, this book aims to induce not merely an understanding of a few simple techniques but a new *approach* to the whole problem of statistical presentation. Properly used, the statistical map or diagram is no mere decoration added as an afterthought to improve the appearance of a piece of work. It must be treated as a highly specialised, often expensive (in time and labour) device which above all is an *integral* part of the task in hand, doing the job it was given to do and doing it not merely satisfactorily but as effectively as possible.

The author's experience in the course of several years' teaching of cartographic techniques to university undergraduates has shown that it is the need for this correct approach which is the most neglected aspect of statistical presentation, so that students frequently show too facile an appraisal of the task in hand, repeatedly using methods so conventional that they have almost become clichés, rather than seeking individual solutions to individual problems. In this they can hardly be blamed. The publications of their elders and betters are by no means immune from the same defect, and existing literature scarcely deals adequately with this need for the inculcation of a correct approach; it is hoped that this book will go some way towards remedying this situation.

Unfortunately for the less specialised person, we are passing today into a period of more intensive usage of statistics than ever before and one which is characterised especially by greater application of mathematical techniques to the figures themselves. In short we are witnessing greatly increased use of those techniques which the mathematician himself would consider part of that branch of his subject which *he* would term 'Statistics'. As its title implies this book is concerned with the *presentation* of statistics and will not consider what might be termed the 'mathematics of statistics'. Two good reasons can be advanced in support of this attitude. In the first place much useful work can be done with statistics, using no more than elementary mathematical knowledge, and it is the author's experience that the inclusion of even a small amount of relatively simple mathematics immediately deters a great many who would otherwise come seeking information. Whilst it cannot be denied that the all-inclusive approach is superior it is dearly bought if it discourages potential users from seeking instruction in that wide variety of techniques which involve nothing more complicated mathematically than long multiplication and long division. The second reason is a more fundamental one. The great majority of advanced mathematical techniques which can be applied to statistics seek to reduce their bulk and determine salient points and trends from within a mass of figures, but even when this simplification has been achieved, the results are not necessarily easy to appreciate and there will frequently arise the need to present them in a more graphic and interesting manner. No amount of advanced mathematics can over-ride the need for instruction in and appreciation of the techniques for *presenting* statistics as well as for *analysing* them, and since the mathematical aspect of statistics is plentifully and well written-up and that of statistical presentation is not, it is on this latter aspect of the problem that the attention of this book is concentrated.

Throughout this book the author has drawn consistently on his own experience, particularly in teaching cartography to undergraduates. The various defects in techniques and mistakes in approach which are described are those which experience has shown to be particularly prone to occur. In so far as it ventures outside the strict considerations of statistical techniques into subjects such as mathematics or source materials this book does so in an attempt to provide information, often of a remarkably elementary nature, which is nevertheless not obtainable easily and quickly from published works in those fields. Whereas the trained mathematician will unhesitatingly obtain the square root of 2543 from a table headed 'Square Roots 10 to 100' nine general readers out of ten would discard this and work out the answer more tediously, using logarithms. In like manner the chapter on source materials (a topic quite plentifully written up elsewhere) tries particularly to provide missing background information, the lack of which has been known to waste many hours of work and cause much frustration and disappointment.

It is not the aim of this book to be encyclopaedic in its nature or dogmatic in its approach. Taken individually, statistical techniques are as elementary in principle as they are complex in application, and consideration of both sides of their nature is essential before successful work can result. Acquaintance with the principle of the technique alone is of little use in itself, just as knowing how to make a motor-car go will not automatically produce a good driver. The statistical cartographer, like the experienced driver, must be prepared to adapt a relatively small store of essential 'know-how' flexibly and individually to the infinitely varied requirements of each situation which he meets. It is the aim of this book to help him to understand both of these aspects of the presentation of statistics.

CHAPTER ONE

Why draw Statistical Maps?

ANYONE who has to prepare a statistical map or diagram might sensibly ask himself at the very outset, 'Why am I drawing this map?'[1] The question is by no means so unnecessary as it may appear at first sight. Of course, no one is likely to embark upon designing anything so complicated, tedious and often expensive, as the average statistical map without having a good reason for doing so, but in practice it is surprisingly easy for this initial aim to be forgotten as the map progresses and more pressing practical difficulties arise and call for a solution.

Many of these practical problems may occur when the designing of the map has scarcely got under way. A suitable technique must be chosen, compatible not only with the statistics themselves, but with the scale of the finished map, which in turn will often be determined by the space available to contain it; from the statistics may come difficulties, such as an excessively large range and inconsistency of definition or accuracy, whilst other problems of presentation may arise from the use of only a limited number of colours, or restriction to black and white only.

All of these are very real problems which must be solved before the designing of the map can proceed, but they should never be allowed to dominate the map so that its initial purpose is subjugated to their solution. It is not uncommon to encounter maps where this has happened; practical difficulties have come to the fore and detail so dominates the map that it becomes a mere formality of illustration in which one cannot 'see the wood for the trees', a poor substitute for the stimulating visual aid to understanding which a well-designed map ought to be.

There is no better way of counteracting this tendency than by starting out with the general aim of the map clearly in mind. The chapters which follow describe many more factors which must be accommodated within the map, but certainly no other single item will be so important in influencing the design as the basic reason for which it was drawn; since considerations of this kind are just as valid when reviewing the design of statistical maps generally as they are when constructing a single example, it is worth while examining, at the very outset, the reasons which cause people to design statistical maps.

Although many particular reasons might be associated with the need for any individual map, most of these will be found to fall within four broad categories which are sufficiently important to be defined first and elaborated afterwards. They are:

---

[1] To avoid tedious repetition the terms 'map' and 'statistical map' may be regarded as including 'diagram' or 'statistical diagram' throughout this book.

1. To arouse greater interest in the subject matter presented.
2. To clarify it, simplify it or explain its more important aspects.
3. To prove a point referred to in text or speech.
4. To act as a statistical 'quarry' for other users.

Of these four aims the first two are widely recognised and in practice almost inseparably linked. They have already been touched upon in the Introduction and need little elaboration. Few items are more unattractive to the eye or more tedious to read than long tables of figures, and unless one has a particularly good head for such things an attempt to read one of these tables may be disappointingly unrewarding. By the time the end of the table is reached the average reader is overwhelmed with information and quite unable easily to answer important questions, such as what were the largest and smallest quantities in the list, where or when did they occur and is there a tendency for groups of similar values or for any exceptional values to be present? The representation of this information in graphical form not only makes the whole subject appear more interesting, but also makes the answers to many of these questions easier to obtain.

The idea of using a statistical device to prove a point is so obvious that it is unlikely completely to be neglected. One does not consciously design a map which gives an entirely wrong impression of the subject under discussion, but it is very easy to be satisfied with too little, and every cartographer ought to ensure that the device used really does prove his point in the most convincing manner. The works manager who draws up a graph of increasing output to impress his board of directors will not choose so cramped a vertical scale that production has to increase by 25% before the line begins to climb at all noticeably when a more generous vertical scale would allow much smaller increases to convey a more forceful impression.[1]

Much the most neglected of these four main reasons is the idea of making the map a statistical quarry, providing a source of information for other purposes than those for which the map was originally designed. The basis of this idea lies in the capacity of the map to act as a remarkably concise summary, able to convey a very great deal of information, the description and implications of which could otherwise be explained only in many pages of text.

This must surely be one of the ideas which underlies the recent appearance of many specialised atlases devoted to individual countries or topics and in which the greater part of the information is displayed in map form. Unfortunately, in so many cases this aim appears to have been lost whilst the atlas was under construction and the mapping of the statistics has come to be regarded as the end point of the process; no provision has been made for the person who wants to 'read back' from the maps to the statistics themselves and it is impossible to adapt and use the material displayed for other research in parallel fields. Fig. 1 illustrates a map which was designed with both this last-mentioned point and the general aim of acting as a statistical 'quarry' very much in mind. Not only is some form of diagrammatic representation used to summarise the main points of the distribution but the actual figures involved are given in shortened form alongside each symbol.

[1] The prudent works manager will not stretch this point too far, of course; an over-generous vertical scale will tend to make even the slightest *fall* in production look alarming and the solution must lie in moderation—or a quickly redrawn version of the graph if production begins to fluctuate.

Fig. 1. Proposals for the Reception of Overspill in England and Wales, Autumn, 1960.

Key to exporting centres: B Birmingham: Bk Blackpool: Bo Bootle: Br Bristol: C Cardiff: G Gateshead: H Hull: L L.C.C. or London area: Ld Leeds: Le Leicester: Lv Liverpool: M Manchester: ME Metropolitan Essex: Mi Middlesbrough: MS Metropolitan Surrey: Mx Middlesex: N Newcastle: Np Newport: O Oldham: R Reading: S Salford: Sh Sheffield: Sm Smethwick: So Southampton: W Walsall: Wo Wolverhampton.

This map was designed to provide, on sight, *detailed* information regarding these proposals, as well as to give some indication of the nature of their distribution. *Source:* Information supplied privately by Local Authorities.

These then are the four great themes which form a basic framework within which the statistical cartographer must work and against which the ideas put forward in the rest of this book must be placed. It is almost self-evident that, expressed in interrogative form, they provide one of the most searching 'acid-tests' with which to measure the success of any individual design.

CHAPTER TWO

Statistical Techniques

ONCE the *raison d'être* of any map has been clearly defined the cartographer is ready to turn to the more practical aspects of its construction. Amongst his first requirements will be a suitable method for presenting the material in question and this chapter attempts to review some of the many techniques which form the starting-point to the practical side of statistical cartography; a knowledge of their variety, the particular purposes to which each is best suited and the difficulties which their application involves is fundamental to the achievement of successful results.

Despite their number the great majority of these techniques are based on extremely simple ideas which are easily understood, but a full appreciation of the value of any one method demands much more than this, involving recognition of such features as its limitations and effectiveness in actual use and the (often) unintentional implications or 'slant' which it may convey to a particular set of figures. Unfortunately, these are factors which are not easily assessed and they may most satisfactorily be approached through consideration of certain basic principles and problems of map design which will be discussed in the later chapters of this book. This chapter will serve simply to introduce the techniques, describe their basic underlying ideas, explain any practical difficulties which may arise in drawing and using them, and consider some of their more individual characteristics.

Unlike the very considerable number of statistical techniques the basic types of statistical problem or distribution which they have to illustrate are relatively few. Moreover, since most of the methods are primarily designed to serve only one or two of these major distributions this offers a useful possibility of classifying their variety and reducing it to manageable proportions. Fig. 2 illustrates such a classification and also suggests a logical order in which to comment on the individual methods. Naturally neither Fig. 2 nor this book as a whole can hope to deal with all the various techniques which have been used to portray statistics, nor is it necessary that they should do so. By confining detailed description to the two dozen or so methods in common use they offer a reasonable guide to the devices most often encountered and at the same time provide sufficiently varied evidence on which to establish a set of principles and deductions which may guide the reader in assessing the effectiveness of any new method he may devise or encounter.

STATISTICAL DIAGRAMS

The first broad subdivision of techniques suggested in Fig. 2 is that into statistical diagrams and statistical maps proper. In the latter category the statistics which are being represented contain an element of spatial distribution which is either so important or so complicated that a base map is need on which this distribution can be recorded. In many cases, however, there is no need to do this; the statistics may refer to one place only or, where several localities are involved, their spatial distribution may be so well known that no representation of it is needed (e.g. in Fig. 9A (p. 30), which shows the six major producers of copper in the world, it is unnecessary to invoke a method which actually shows where such places as Chile and the Congo are).

Techniques falling into this second broad category will be referred to in this book as statistical diagrams. Strictly speaking this term should also include the many, often complicated, techniques which belong to that branch of mathematics known as statistics, but these are regarded as falling outside the scope of a work of this kind which, as explained in the Introduction, deals only with simple methods capable of being understood without mathematical training. The division into 'maps' and 'diagrams' is not entirely a rigid one. It will be seen later that statistical diagrams are often incorporated into techniques which have a map as their basis, but this slight degree of overlap need cause no confusion.

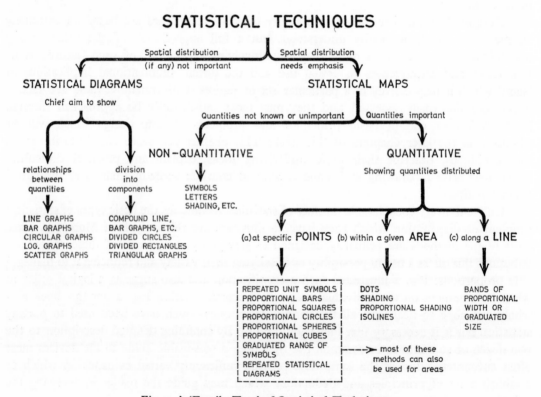

Fig. 2. A 'Family Tree' of Statistical Techniques.

TECHNIQUES SHOWING RELATIONSHIPS BETWEEN QUANTITIES

The various techniques comprised within the category of statistical diagrams can themselves be divided into two major groups, although this division is not a precise one. The distinction is basically between those methods which are concerned with showing the relationships between varying quantities and those which indicate the portion of the whole formed by several component parts.

In both divisions the various members of the graph family are well represented and since many methods in the first category can easily be adapted to perform the functions of the second they will be considered in their simpler form first and elaborated later.

LINE GRAPHS

Sooner or later most people encounter the simple line graph. Patients in hospital craning their necks to read a temperature chart and dripping holiday-makers hopefully examining the barograph on a rain-swept promenade are alike seeking reassurance from this elementary but effective device. The principle behind it is simple. Graphs show the way in which changes in one quantity—the patient's temperature or the height of the barometer—are related to changes in another quantity—in both these cases time. Mathematicians call these changing quantities *variables* and furthermore speak of one as the *dependent* and the other as the *independent* variable. The distinction is not difficult to understand. In most cases where simple graphs are used it will be noticed that one variable (the independent), e.g. time, changes steadily and regularly whereas the second (the dependent), e.g. temperature or pressure, changes more irregularly and may even be controlled by the first. It is usual when plotting information as a simple line graph to plot the independent variable on the horizontal scale, and the dependent variable on the vertical scale.

The basis of any graph is a series of values for the two variables plotted along two scales drawn at right angles; the name *line graph* is derived from the practice of emphasising the relationship between these plotted values by joining the dots either by a smoothly curved line which passes easily without arbitrary changes of direction through all plotted points (as in Fig. 3A) or, alternatively, by a series of straight lines drawn between the plotted values (see Fig. 3B). The line attracts attention to such features as maximum and minimum values and particularly to the tendency of values to rise or fall on any part of the graph. Normally the smooth curve is used only if the values plotted are part of a steadily changing relationship for which it might be desirable to determine intermediate values which were not actually recorded. Fig. 3A shows such a graph illustrating the height of river level and the passage of a flood on one of the tributaries of the Tennessee River in 1875. A smooth curve was needed here between the plotted points to record the *gradual* rise, passing of the main flood wave and its recession, including the temporary slackening in the rate of recession which occurred between March 3rd and 6th. Straight lines drawn between plotted points would have given sharp arbitrary peaks which could not have occurred in practice, and intermediate values which were either too high or too low according to whether the trend of the graph was concave or convex. The smoothly drawn curve allows accurate deduction of such information as the length of time during which the river level was above bank height (or any other particular height, e.g. the height of any contemplated flood defences), even though the precise moments at which these levels were exceeded were not recorded in the series of values from which the graph was plotted.

Fig. 3. Types of Simple Line and Bar Graph. *Sources: Fig. 3A.* G. F. White (ed.), *Papers on Flood Problems,* Chicago, 1961. *Fig. 3B. The Guardian,* June 6th, 1961. *Fig. 3C.* U.S. Bureau of the Census, *Historical Statistics of the United States, Colonial Times to 1957,* Washington, D.C., 1960. *Fig. 3D.* Registrar-General, *Census of England and Wales, 1951,* County Volumes Staffordshire and Hampshire, London (H.M.S.O.), 1954.

Unless accurate interpolations of this kind are required from a graph the refinement of using a smooth curve to join up plotted values is not necessary. In many instances not only are intermediate values not required but it may be quite impossible for them to occur, as for example where figures refer to monthly or yearly totals; in these cases a straight line joining the plotted values is all that is required.

Although graphs are usually *constructed* on graph paper (commonly obtainable with squares of $\frac{1}{4}$-in., $\frac{1}{8}$-in., $\frac{1}{10}$-in. and 1-mm. side) it is customary today to *publish* them on a blank background. In the past the 'graph paper background' was frequently reproduced as well, but the appearance was often rather heavy and fussy, detracting from the main message of the graph. Unfortunately, the contemporary trend represents a swing too much in the other direction, and it is not uncommon to encounter graphs on which the only positive indication of the values of the dependent variable (the quantity on the graph which arouses most interest) is a single, often badly calibrated, vertical scale at the extreme left-hand edge of the graph, a rather niggardly provision which makes it difficult for anyone to estimate values from the graph for his own purposes. If one dismisses as superfluous the old graph-paper lines which formerly carried values right across the face of the graph, the very least which can be attempted is to add a second vertical scale at the right-hand edge, so that a ruler placed across the graph from the two scales will easily allow values to be determined. It is also often useful to rule and mark two or three horizontal lines at values which are particularly relevant to the trends on the graph and to mark, in figures against the line, the values of any important maxima, minima or points at which the trends of the graph show important changes. On Fig. 3B the values 106 and 116 are inserted to emphasise that most of the indexes shown fluctuate only between these two limits whilst the maximum (125) and the minimum (97) of the index for durable goods, the most important feature on the graph, are also marked. The aim is to present a more detailed portrayal of the situation than the rather bald message which derives from the shape of the lines alone.

It is occasionally possible to write on the face of the graph the value of every point from which the graph was constructed. Where this is done the value is often marked by a large dot whilst the lines between the dots can be drawn thick and heavy, stopping just short of the dots. This is a very bold style of graph which would normally be dismissed as too heavy for accurate reading, but where the values are added this point is no longer valid and the whole of the design of the graph can be orientated towards producing a forceful impression. Figure 5A (p. 21) illustrates such a graph.

Where the number of illustrations is restricted, or where comparisons are important, several items can be plotted on the same graph, though this practice can easily be abused. The more detail there is on any graph the more difficult will it be for the eye to single out the important features of any one line, and if the lines overlap at all the impression can become confused as can be seen on Fig. 3B. Here, though individual lines can be traced, the characteristics of each are only obvious after fairly close examination. This is generally a disadvantage, but may not always be so; in Fig. 3B itself the confused effect actually helps to put over the main message of the graph which seeks to show the way in which sales of durable goods have stood out distinctively from other main groups. Alternatively if the various quantities shown occur in different parts of the graph then a considerable number of lines can be accommodated without causing confusion.

It is not uncommon for two vertical scales to be needed on the same graph, e.g. where two quantities expressed in different units have to be recorded, as in Fig. 4A. In this case the two vertical scales are quite independent and can be designed so that the two lines of the graph are close together or widely separated, whichever may be desired.

In Fig. 4A the two vertical scales refer to quite different units—namely, square metres of cloth and metric tons of yarn, and this causes no confusion; generally speaking it is not desirable to incorporate on one graph two different vertical scales for the *same* units, however tempting this may be. The result will almost certainly produce a strongly misleading visual image which will not easily be totally overcome. Fig. 4B shows recent world production of aluminium and magnesium, two metals frequently alloyed together and of common interest to modern technologists because of their lightness. Unfortunately, production of magnesium

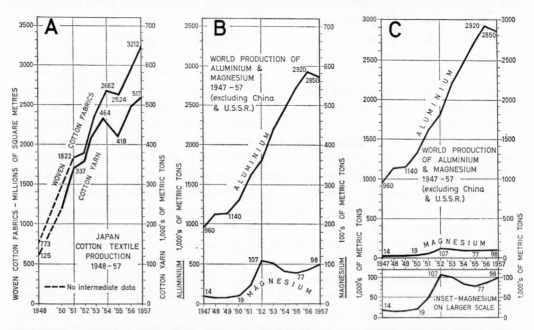

Fig. 4. Aspects of Vertical Scales on Line Graphs. *Fig. 4A.* Two different vertical scales for two different units. *Fig. 4B.* Two different vertical scales for the same units. *Fig. 4C.* An improved method of presenting the information in Fig. 4B. *Sources:* United Nations, *Statistical Year Book, 1958,* New York, 1958.

is much less than that of aluminium so that there is a strong temptation, if the two are graphed together, to use a different vertical scale for magnesium. As Fig. 4B shows, even when significant values are added to the graph it is not easy to counteract the first impressions which one receives of the relative magnitude of production of the two metals in any one year. In 1952 magnesium production seems to be about one-third of that of aluminium, whereas in fact it was about one-twentieth. A better solution to the problem is shown in Fig. 4C where the two are graphed comparably, but an 'inset' graph on a more generous vertical scale is also added for magnesium.

Whether one or two vertical scales are in use on a graph it is important that the vertical scale or scales should start at zero, if changes in values are to be seen in their true proportion. Unless this is done the graph can exaggerate small changes so that it is impossible to get any real idea of their significance. Occasionally the changes may be sufficiently important on their own to need graphing in this way or, as Fig. 5A shows, there may be an ulterior motive in doing so, but in most cases a more sensible picture will be obtained by allowing the vertical scale to show the whole range of values from zero (see Fig. 5B).[1]

Fig. 5. Two different ways of portraying the same information may produce two quite different impressions. Fig. 5A attempts to exaggerate the importance of changes, whereas Fig. 5B shows these in their true proportions. The designation 'steady' may not satisfy all ratepayers, but it at least presents the situation in rather a better light.

BAR GRAPHS

Very similar indeed to the line graph is the *bar graph*, an example of which is shown in Fig. 3C (p. 18). It originates in the same way from a series of values plotted against two axes, but in this case instead of being joined by a line the values are represented by a series of vertical bars which run from the plotted points to the foot of the vertical scale. Usually each bar is kept distinct from its neighbour, but this is not absolutely necessary.

The effect is rather similar to the line graph if only for the reason that the tops of the bars trace out rise and fall of the total, but on the other hand the presence of the bars themselves attracts attention to the actual *quantities*, whereas the line graph attracts the eye away

[1] This example is not entirely fanciful. Fig. 5A was suggested by an actual poster pushed through the author's letter-box during the course o fan election campaign.

from the quantities and towards the rise and fall of the values. Quite apart from this rather subtle, psychological distinction the bar graph has certain other advantages. It is particularly suitable where the data represent values (e.g. total annual output of any commodity or total rainfall in any one month) which are quite separate and distinct from the preceding and succeeding ones, the break between the bars emphasising this distinction. In Fig. 3C the use of the bar graph technique also makes it easier to emphasise the fact that after 1920 the data changed from a 10- to a 5-yearly basis, than would have been the case with a line graph.

In very many cases, however, the bar graph and line graph are interchangeable and the kind of considerations which apply to such features as vertical scales, adding pertinent values, etc., in the line graph apply equally here. Thus on Fig. 3C a line has been ruled across the bars every 200 million acres to help estimation of values and, incidentally, to emphasise the date when the amount of grazing land fell below these levels.

Although line graphs are almost invariably drawn using the vertical scale for the dependent variable, this rule is frequently ignored where bar graphs are concerned and these are often to be seen 'turned on their side', with horizontal bars, as in Fig. 3D (p. 18). Not the least advantage of this practice is the ease with which such features as dates, names and values can be written in when the bars are horizontal, whereas the narrow vertical bar often allows this only if the printing is made to stand on end.

As with the line graph it is possible to show two or more items on the same bar graph. The usual procedure is to place the bars for the various items side by side, but it will be appreciated that if more than three variables are recorded each bar becomes separated from its predecessor and successor by rather a large gap so that it is not always easy for the eye to follow trends as well as values. This disadvantage can partly be overcome by slightly overlapping the bars, but even so this is one instance in which the line graph has a definite advantage over the bar graph.

CIRCULAR GRAPHS

It may sometimes happen that a series of values which has to be plotted relates to a recurrent state of affairs. The most commonly encountered data of this kind are figures for mean monthly temperature and rainfall though other examples are not difficult to imagine; a large store will normally vary the proportion of its staff employed in different departments throughout the year and might prepare figures to show the average percentage of the staff employed in any given department each month throughout the year; similar data could relate to labour employed in the various operations on a farm.

Where cyclic features of this kind occur, their representation by normal line or bar graphs has certain disadvantages, notably that the left and right hand edges of the graph break what is manifestly a continuum and may make it difficult to appreciate trends at a critical time. It is surely a major defect that with climatic statistics relating to the northern hemisphere and presented in the usual manner the winter half of the régime can only be seen by piecing together two separate portions; in the southern hemisphere matters are worse, for it is the figures for the more important summer growing season which are interrupted.

It is a simple matter to overcome this objection by devising a circular form of the normal graph and the result has been variously called a circular graph, clock graph or polar chart.

The basic idea is simply that of taking the normal graph and stretching and bending it so that the two outer edges meet. Values now increase radially outwards and it is usual to make zero a small circle since this makes drawing easier than if zero were placed at the very centre of the circle. Fig. 6 illustrates such a graph showing mean monthly temperature and rainfall figures for Fez in Morocco, a station which is particularly poorly served by normal methods because of the way in which they interrupt the representation of the winter rainfall with its peculiar double maximum.

Generally speaking, circular graphs are not widely used. Though they may overcome the disadvantages described above they bring additional handicaps which render them less attractive. The greatest of these is that the easily appreciated rise and fall of the normal graph is replaced by the idea of a line moving away from or towards the centre of the circle and considerable practice is needed before its message can be appreciated in detail. It is not easy in Fig. 6A to form much of an impression about what is happening in the yearly temperature régime at Fez, and even with the less difficult bar graphs for rainfall their divergent nature weakens the side-by-side type of comparison. On the whole the disadvantages of interrupting cyclic phenomena can be more easily overcome by graphing $1\frac{1}{2}$ (or even 2) cycles in the normal way, as in Fig. 6B, although where this is done the end of each cycle should be clearly marked to avoid confusion.

The circular graph is the first example we have met of a feature which

Fig. 6. Fig. 6A. A Circular Graph or Polar Chart— Mean Monthly Temperature and Rainfall at Fez, Morocco. Fig. 6B. An alternative method of presenting the same information. *Source:* Kendrew W. G.: *Climates of the Continents,* 4th Edition, Oxford, 1953.

occurs more widely than it should in statistical techniques—namely, a method which is perfectly sound, even logical, mathematically, but which, visually, is rather ineffective.

LOGARITHMIC GRAPHS

So far we have considered graphs in which changes in *quantity* were all-important, i.e. where we wish to compare actual *amounts* of increase and decrease. This is not always the case. For example, an efficiency expert comparing changes in output at two factories after new methods of working have been introduced will not be interested simply in increase in the *amount* of production since one factory may be much bigger than the other and would natu-rally show a greater numerical increase. What is needed is some method of assessing the *rate* of increase rather than the amount; if output from the smaller factory has trebled and that from the larger only doubled, the new methods have obviously been more successful in the former whatever the quantities produced may seem to indicate.

The need to pay attention to *rate* of increase as well as amount is quite common and it is interesting to consider how this problem could be presented graphically. Unfortunately, in studies of this kind the ordinary line graph is not only useless but sometimes positively misleading. Consider another example. At two villages X and Y the populations at three successive censuses were 100, 200 and 400 and 50, 100 and 200 respectively. In which village is the population increasing most rapidly? Graphed in the normal manner, as in Fig. 7A, the impression is given that the population in X is increasing far faster than in Y, particularly so between 1921 and 1931. This is quite true, numerically, but a glance at the figures will soon indicate that in fact *both* villages have *consistently* shown the *same* rate of increase, each doubling its population every ten years. The line graph is not particularly successful here; what is needed is another sort of graph which will *show equal rates of change by lines of equal slope*, whatever the numerical basis of that change may be.

The logarithmic graph is such a device, and an example is shown in Fig. 7D; though at first sight it appears a little strange it is not difficult to understand once the basic idea is grasped. So far as the horizontal scale is concerned all is quite normal;[1] it is in the vertical scale that changes are introduced. Here the numbers are not spaced evenly, e.g. in Fig. 7B the interval between 20 and 30 is slightly less than that between 10 and 20 and the same amount separates 200 and 300 higher up the scale. This is because on the vertical scale of a logarithmic graph numbers are spaced not according to the difference between them but *according to the difference between their logarithms*. Fig. 7C shows how this arrangement works and Fig. 7D the kind of graph that results, characterised by a gradual and regular 'bunching' of lines on the vertical scale.

Each of these regular bunchings is called a *cycle* and it will be noticed that the top and bottom line of each cycle must be 10 or some multiple or decimal of 10, e.g. 100, 10,000, 1, 0·01. Each time a new cycle is added to the graph the value at the top is 10 times greater than that at the bottom and it follows from this that going down the scale, however many cycles are added, *zero can never be reached on a logarithmic graph*.

Although it is perfectly possible to draw out one's own vertical scale for a logarithmic graph by spacing values according to their logarithms obtained from mathematical tables this is a tedious process and these graphs are usually plotted on specially ruled graph paper. Such paper is not of uniform character, for both the number of cycles on the vertical scale and the spacing of lines on the horizontal scale can vary and it is usually described by speci-fying these two quantities, e.g. 4 cycles $\times \frac{1}{8}$ in. or 3 cycles $\times \frac{1}{10}$ in., the latter figure referring to spacing on the horizontal scale.

Fig. 7D redraws logarithmically the figures for world production of aluminium and magnesium already encountered in Fig. 4C (p. 20) and enables interesting comparisons

---

[1] In another type of logarithmic graph both vertical and horizontal scales are logarithmic, but such a device falls outside the scope of this book.

Fig. 7. The Logarithmic Graph. *Figs. 7A and 7B*: The same information graphed 'normally' (Fig. 7A) and logarithmically (Fig. 7B) *Fig. 7C.* How a logarithmic graph is devised. *Fig. 7D.* The information formerly presented in Figs. 4B and 4C graphed logarithmically to allow rates of change in annual output to be deduced and compared. *Source:* Fig. 7D. United Nations: *Statistical Year Book, 1958*; New York, 1958.

to be made not between *amount* of production but of *rates of change* of production and *fluctuations*. In Fig. 4C world production of magnesium misleadingly appeared rather steady; Fig. 7D shows it to be subject to quite violent fluctuations regularly rising or falling by between 10% and 25% each year though showing a sustained increase of more than 100% per year between 1950 and 1952. On the other hand aluminium, with a more established position in world technology, shows a remarkably steady expansion at between 20 and 25% per annum for most of the period up to 1956. It is not difficult to add to a logarithmic graph a scale indicating the slopes produced by typical percentage increases and decreases and this has been done in Fig. 7D to help estimation.

The use of logarithmic graph paper is sometimes advocated as one way of graphing figures which contain a large vertical range which would be difficult to accommodate on the normal line graph. The rapid rate of increase on the vertical scale of the logarithmic graph is very tempting here, but this use is not to be advocated; a logarithmic graph is a specialised device for fulfilling a particular need and should be used as such. It is not without its drawbacks—the man in the street is inclined to be highly suspicious of graphs with peculiar vertical scales and logarithmic graphs are not likely ever to be accepted popularly as line graphs are—but for performing its particular task it has no substitute and it might with advantage be rather more widely used than is the case at present.

SCATTER GRAPHS

The logarithmic graph is a mathematician's device which it is not too difficult for the layman to understand; the same can be said of the scatter graph. True, to obtain the finer implications of this device, or the most accurate deductions from it, considerable mathematical knowledge is needed, but it has nevertheless several simple uses and functions which the layman can understand quite easily, and these simpler aspects will be covered in this book.

The graphs which have been studied so far are used in determining the relationship between a series of *several* values for two variables related to *one* place, example or commodity. It is not difficult to envisage a slightly different kind of investigation where there is only *one* value for each of the two variables, but this is known for *several* places. Each value can still be plotted against scales drawn on two axes at right angles in the usual way, but in this case there is no question of joining the points by a line since no continuity is involved and each example is separate and distinct. All that we have, therefore, from which to read the message of this graph is a scatter of points, hence its common title of 'scatter graph'.

The scatter graph is used to investigate what sort of relationship, if any, exists between two variables which occur over a wide area. It could be used, for example, to see if there is any clear relationship between birth-rate and standard of living in the various countries of the world, total population and number of persons employed in service industry in a group of towns, size of factory and output per worker in a group of factories in the same industry, and so on.

Any such relationship has to be deduced from the patterns which the scatter of dots shows when the values are plotted. If the dots show a random scatter, with no grouping or obvious trends, as in Fig. 8B, then no systematic relationship exists between the two variables under investigation. On the other hand the dots may show a marked tendency to form groups, as in Fig. 8C where two main groups may be distinguished. The very fact of the proximity of the plotted values on the graph indicates that here are places which are very similar in this respect, and the simplest possible use of the scatter graph is in defining groups of similar places without attempting to carry the investigation any further. The essential implication of Fig. 8C is that the places under investigation tend to fall very markedly into two main groups. This might lead to further research to determine reasons for this grouping and

Fig. 8. The Scatter Graph. *Fig. 8A.* A Scatter Graph to indicate the relationship between percentage change in population and percentage change in the number of dwellings in parishes in South Lincolnshire 1931-51. *Figs. 8B, C and D.* Characteristic types of 'scatter'. *Source:* Fig 8A. Registrar-General, *Census of England and Wales, 1951*, County Volume, Lincolnshire, London (H.M.S.O.), 1955.

also for the few examples on the graph which noticeably fall outside these groups, the very isolation of these values stressing their peculiarity. An example of the use of the scatter graph for grouping data will be described later, in Chapter 6.

A rather more usual tendency than that illustrated in Fig. 8C is for the plotted values to be along a line or, more commonly, within a narrow linear zone, as in Figs. 8A and D, and where this occurs it is often possible to express the relationship between the two variables in the form of a mathematical formula. To do so it is necessary to replace the scatter of dots by a single line, either straight or curved, which represents the best average fit through the points on the graph. This is the most important part of the whole process, for the accuracy with which the 'best fit' is obtained seriously affects the nature of any subsequent formula. Not unnaturally, mathematicians have developed rather complicated ways of establishing this best fit and of deducing the significance of the resultant line, but even the person with little mathematical training can make elementary deductions from a reasonably drawn line, provided he is content not to interpret his findings too pedantically or regard them as more than a general guide to a situation. For example, if the plotted points lie in a rather broad linear zone the line of best fit will be a fairly weak one with the resultant relationship rather unreliable, and vice versa.

Let us consider a fairly simple investigation of the implications of Fig. 8A which was drawn in an attempt to establish whether any relationship exists, in a rural area in south Lincolnshire, between changes in the population of a parish and the number of dwellings it contained, for the period 1931-51. If such a relationship could be demonstrated (and it seemed reasonable to suppose that it would continue beyond 1951) then the results could be used, for example, by the Local Planning Authority as a guide to the number of houses which would be needed in any area to maintain its population, or the possible consequences of allowing only a limited increase in the number of dwellings in an area.

Inspection of the scatter of points on Fig. 8A shows immediately that these run in a fairly narrow zone inclined upwards across the graph from left to right and at least in the left-hand portion of the graph a straight line of best fit can be drawn through the plotted values, paying particular attention to the more reliable ones for the larger villages. This line represents the average tendency of the plotted values, indicates that some relationship does seem to exist between the two quantities and suggests important conclusions such as the fact that until an increase of more than about 18% has occurred in the number of dwellings no increase in population is likely; conversely, if the number of dwellings stays stationary, a decrease in population of about 20% can be expected. The line also releases intermediate values, e.g. an increase in population of 10% is usually associated with an increase of about 25% in dwellings.

So long as the line remains straight it is not too difficult to establish a formula which will describe it. Mathematicians say that all relationships which appear on a graph as a straight line will follow the general formula

$$y = mx + c$$

This is simply a shorthand way of saying 'to find the value of the variable on the vertical axis (y-axis) take the value of the variable on the horizontal axis (x-axis), multiply it by a factor (m) and add to it something else (c)'. m and c are fairly easily determined. m is simply the gradient of the line, regarded as *positive* if it slopes *upwards from left to right*, and vice versa; c is what might be called the 'zero error'—namely, the value on the y-axis when the value on the x-axis is 0. Thus in Fig. 8A the gradient of the line can be measured in the usual way (e.g. in the 'hill' where the line crosses the two axes it rises about 18 units vertically while travelling 19 horizontally) and is 18/19; similarly c is also $+18$ and the formula would read

$$y = 18/19x + 18$$

The advantage of the formula over the graph lies in the fact that it is much easier to memorise and can be used without the actual graph being present.

Although the left-hand portion of Fig. 8A shows fairly steady relationships of the kind just described complications arise in the right-hand portion. Here the 'straight-line tendency' breaks down and the zone tends to fork, one half more or less continuing the original trend, but the other curving upwards much more steeply. When this occurs it is worth while going back to the original idea of using a scatter graph to distinguish between different kinds of things and looking to see if there is any logical reason for the distinction between the two groups. Investigation shows that in this case this might be so, for the members of the upper group are almost entirely Fenland parishes while those in the lower one are hill parishes, although here the number is so small that it is difficult to decide whether they constitute a valid trend at all.

Once curved lines are introduced, mathematical relationships are beyond the ability of the layman to deduce (although one could say that in the Fenland villages the trend changes and closely approximates to another formula ($y = 50/18x + 0$), but the example has been taken far enough to show that the scatter graph has a good deal of information to offer. In this case we have obtained a formula[1] which is reasonably typical of the greater part of the range of values likely to be encountered and have had our attention attracted towards lines of further investigation such as the possibility of a fundamental difference in the dwelling-people relationship in Fenland and hill parishes (e.g. variations in the ratio of private to council houses or tenanted to owner-occupied property) and the reasons for exceptional values, e.g. Great Ponton, Carlby, Horbling and Easton, which stand out from the rest. In the investigation of a relationship of this kind, which cannot be other than relatively imperfect because of widely varying local conditions, quite sensible results can be obtained by the layman without any need to introduce higher mathematics.

TECHNIQUES SHOWING PROPORTIONS FORMED BY CONSTITUENT PARTS

The second main purpose to which the simpler statistical techniques are devoted is that of indicating the part which various components play in forming the whole. This is normally a relatively simple problem and as several of the techniques are derived from ideas already encountered they can be fairly briefly described.

COMPOUND LINE AND BAR GRAPHS

So long as the vertical scale on a simple line or bar graph commences at zero it will be possible to subdivide the area beneath the line or contained within the bar into any number of component parts; the result can be called a compound line or bar graph and examples are illustrated in Fig. 9.

The basic principle is a simple one, deceptively simple in practice, for the subdivision should be attempted in moderation and with some forethought if the result is not to be

---

[1] With a rather general relationship such as the one analysed here little would be lost if this formula, once obtained, was rewritten as $y = $ (approximately) $x + 18$ since 18/19 can be regarded as near enough to unity.

mathematically exact but visually disappointing. It is by no means easy on such compound graphs to follow the trend of increase or decrease in all the components. A glance at Fig. 9 will show that the only component whose trends can *certainly* be observed easily is the bottom one, which has a horizontal line at its base; the others must be assessed as spaces between pairs of lines, which may be increasing or decreasing at different rates and moving

Fig. 9. Compound Line and Bar Graphs to illustrate component parts. Figs. 9B and 9D portray, in a more satisfactory and legible manner, the information contained in Figs. 9A and 9C. *Source:* Figs. 9A and 9B J. C. Weaver and F. E. Lukermann, *World Resource Statistics*, Minneapolis, 1953. Figs. 9C and 9D L. D. Stamp and S. H. Beaver, *The British Isles* (First and Third Editions), London, 1933 and 1941.

to different levels on the graph, according to the accident of the total of the components which lie beneath them. In the case of the bar graph all the lines remain horizontal but the individual sections may bob up and down making side-by-side comparisons less simple.

    The best defence against this is to devote some attention to the *order* in which the components are taken. The order in which they appear in the published statistics is unlikely to be the best one for this purpose and the most satisfactory arrangement is to plot *the most stable elements at the bottom,* thus ensuring that vertical movements are damped down for as long as possible. Figs. 9B and D show redrawn versions of Figs. 9A and C where this principle has been observed. Both are considerably easier to read than their predecessors, especially Fig. 9D where side-by-side comparisons are now quite easily made. Between 1927 and 1932 fluctuations in world copper production were almost entirely confined to the U.S. component, though in Fig. 9A this immediately 'tilts' the representation of all the other producers; similarly, and not unnaturally in the largest producer, production in the U.S.A. tended to fluctuate more than in most other countries and the effect of this at the base of the graph is responsible for most of the 'ups and downs' of the other components. If, however, one component is of much more interest than any of the others it should be placed at the bottom of the graph and the general rule of arrangement modified accordingly.

DIVIDED CIRCLES OR PIE GRAPHS

The divided circle, or pie graph as it is almost always called, is one of the commonest statistical diagrams. The total quantity concerned is represented by a circle which is divided into segments proportional in size to the components; comparisons can be made between fluctuations in these components in two or more examples if a circle, subdivided in this way, is drawn for each of them. If proportion alone is important each of the circles can be of the same size, but it is rather more common to use circles of varying size so that the area of each is proportional to the total quantity which they represent. In this way the two elements of quantity and subdivision are both reflected in the result.

Fig. 10 shows in this manner how the four main source areas of overspill population in England and Wales have utilised different kinds of reception areas for this population. Comparison between the part played by any type of reception area in the four cases must be made by comparing the *angle* which that sector of the circle occupies in each case.

Perhaps the most unexpected feature of pie graphs is the quite considerable amount of simple calculations involved if they are used in any quantity. Normally, three distinct stages are involved before plotting can begin; these are:

(1) A circle must be drawn proportional in area to the total quantity to be represented.
(2) Each component part must be expressed as a decimal or percentage of the whole.
(3) The angle which corresponds to this decimal or percentage of 360° (for that is, of course, the total angle available for subdivision at the centre of the circle) must be calculated.

Thus 8 entities each with 7 components will mean 8 calculations under (1) above and 56 under (2) and (3), but fortunately tables can be used to avoid some of this work.

The simplest of these calculations is that involved in stage 1. To draw a series of circles whose areas are proportional to given quantities all that is necessary is to look up the square root of each quantity and use this number, converted into suitable units such as millimetres of $\frac{1}{100}$ths of an inch, as the radius of the circle. There is no need to introduce π into these calculations since the circles must not have an *absolute* area but only be *proportional* in size. Tables of square roots are normally incorporated in four-figure mathematical tables, usually in the form of two pages, the first giving square roots from 1 to 10, the second from 10 to 100, but in fact these can be used to find the square root of *any* number. Square roots of numbers with an *odd number of digits before the decimal point* should be sought in the pages showing *square roots 1 to 10*, those of numbers with an *even number of digits before the decimal point* on the pages *square roots 10 to 100*. For numbers greater than 100 the printed position of the decimal point in the square root tables should of course be ignored and its true position found by inspection, e.g. to find the square root of 53,426·28.

1. If four-figure tables are being used reduce the numbers to four significant figures, i.e. 53,430·00.

2. There are 5 digits before the decimal point. On the 1 to 10 page the square root corresponding to 5,343 is 2,312.

3. Since 100^2 is 10,000 and $1,000^2$ is 1,000,000 the square root of 53,430 must lie between 100 and 1,000 and the decimal point must therefore be placed to give the answer: 231·2.

Unfortunately, calculation cannot be simplified in stage 2, although a slide-rule will supply sufficiently accurate information quickly and easily

Fig. 10. Divided Circles (Pie Graphs) and Divided Rectangles —Types of Reception Area proposed for Overspill from Different Sources in England and Wales. The figures in the rectangular diagram refer to 1,000's of houses. *Source:* Information supplied privately by Local Authorities.

here. Stage 3, however, can be greatly simplified either by using a percentage protractor, i.e. one graduated in percentages not in degrees, or by using the table given below. For this purpose the component must be expressed as a decimal of the whole to three significant figures. If these figures are termed, A, B and C the corresponding angle can rapidly be deduced from the table in the manner shown.

A TABLE FOR CONVERTING DECIMALS OF A CIRCLE INTO DEGREES

	Table One		Table Two				Example:
A	Value used	BC	Value used	BC	Value used		
1	36°	03	1°	53	19°		
2	72°	06	2°	56	20°		
3	108°	08	3°	58	21°		Express ·371 of a circle as
4	144°	11	4°	61	22°		degrees.
5	180°	14	5°	64	23°		Call ·371 ABC, therefore A=3
6	216°	17	6°	67	24°		and BC=71.
7	252°	19	7°	69	25°		
8	288°	22	8°	72	26°		If A=3 value used is 108°.
9	324°	25	9°	75	27°		If BC=71 no value is given.
		28	10°	78	28°		Take nearest value to 71, i.e.
		31	11°	81	29°		BC=72 when value used is 26°.
		33	12°	83	30°		Add these two values.
		36	13°	86	31°		*Answer is* 134°.
		39	14°	89	32°		
		42	15°	92	33°		
		44	16°	94	34°		
		47	17°	97	35°		
		50	18°	00	00°		

DIVIDED RECTANGLES

It is a simple step from the divided circle to the divided rectangle and the basic principle of this idea has already been encountered in the subdivided bar of the compound bar graph. In this case a rectangle (whose area may be made proportional to the total quantity) replaces the circle and can be subdivided into layers, each representing one of the components.

It is rather surprising that the divided circle is much more commonly encountered than the divided rectangle, for the latter has a certain advantage when comparisons have to be made between several examples. This derives from the fact that whereas a circle has only one dimension which can be varied, the radius, the rectangle has two and variations in area can be accommodated by altering only one of these and keeping the other (usually the height) uniform. If this uniform vertical height is made to equal 100 units of any kind and the components are expressed as percentages, both subdivision and subsequent comparison will be easy; moreover, the several examples can be placed completely side by side within one block, which can also show a scale of percentages on the vertical edge and even, if required, a scale of quantity along the horizontal edge. Fig. 10 shows the same information presented in both forms and amply illustrates the superiority of the divided rectangle over the pie graph for side-by-side comparative purposes. It can be argued, however, that if the devices have to be widely scattered, e.g. over the face of a map, comparison is slightly easier between divided circles than divided rectangles.

THE TRIANGULAR GRAPH

The triangular graph is a statistical device which has several facets to its character. In certain respects it can be considered as a variety of graph which is able to show three variables instead of the usual two, and in both interpretation and use it has strong affinities to the scatter graph; alternatively, since the three variables must be expressed as percentages adding up to 100% in total, the graph can be considered as being primarily concerned to show varying proportions as part of the whole.

As Fig. 11A shows, the basic idea is once again easily understood. In form the graph consists of an equilateral triangle with sides 100 units long, each carrying a scale running from 0 to 100. Each point of the triangle acts as both *100 for one scale and 0 for another* and the scales usually increase in a clockwise direction along each side. As in the normal graph these scale values are carried across the graph by lines, not in this case all horizontal but inclined to each scale line at an angle of 60°; the direction of the line through 0 on any scale is given by the adjacent side of the triangle and the rest of the lines applying to that scale run parallel to the line through 0.

If the scales are correctly drawn and numbered it will be found that any combination of three variables, so long as they add up to 100, will be represented by only one point. In plotting it is best to start with one component, find its value on the appropriate scale and carry this line across the graph until it meets a line corresponding to the value of the next component on its scale. There is no need to bother about the third component since the plotted point will automatically be correctly situated in relation to the third scale.

Triangular graphs are used to study the way in which three components or variables occur throughout a wide series of examples. They can be used, for example, to study variations in the proportion of sand, silt and clay in soils, or primary, secondary and tertiary industry in the industrial structure of a series of towns, provided that these three components form the whole content of the soil or the industrial employment respectively. The most normal requirement when proportions are analysed by means of a triangular graph is to establish the existence or otherwise of groups of similar places so that some sort of classification can be produced. Once these groups are recognised their position on the graph will also suggest a description of their nature, but a little practice is needed before most observers can read the graph easily. Figs. 11B, c and D try to give some help in this respect by emphasising the implications of location in certain zones of the graph, e.g. a location close to one of the *points* of the triangle implies that one component must be very large, whilst location close to a *side* of the triangle indicates that one component is quite small. In each case it is wisest to check just which component is large or small carefully from the scales at the side of the graph, but if Figs. 11B and c are kept in mind when analysing any scatter of points on the graph they will be found most useful in translating the pattern into everyday language.

As an example of the working of this device Fig. 11A can be used to study the way in which employment in the twelve main industrial activities in Sweden is divided amongst small, medium-sized and large[1] factories, and Fig. 11D shows the same values against the background of lines which have been used in Figs. 11B and C. It will be seen at once that

Fig. 11. The Triangular Graph. *Fig. 11A.* Proportion of workers in small, medium and large sized factories in the main industrial groups in Sweden. *Figs. 11B and 11C.* Significance of position in different parts of the triangle. *Fig. 11D.* Points plotted on Fig. 11A in relation to areas marked on Figs. 11B and 11C. *Source:* Statistiska Centralbyran, *Statistisk Arsbok för Sverige,* 1960, Stockholm, 1960.

in this respect Swedish industry tends to fall into three groups, with the metal and engineering industry standing rather distinctively outside these. One of these groups, containing the quarrying, printing, wood-working, food and drink industries is characteristically dominated by small factories which never provide less than about 55% of the total employment, whilst large factories are almost entirely absent. The second group, which contains the leather, gas, water and electricity, chemicals and textile industries is not dominated by any single component, but tends to have a fairly low proportion of large factories and a very even division of the bulk of the jobs between small- and medium-sized works. In mining and pulp and paper there is again fairly even division, this time between large- and medium-sized factories with very few small ones.

[1] In this example limiting values of 100 and 500 employees were used to define the three categories.

STATISTICAL MAPS

Within the limits of the basic principles of its design, almost every type of statistical diagram allows its designer relatively wide freedom of action. In marked contrast to this, as soon as a map is used as the basis for any composition, a rigid framework is introduced which will exert considerable influence over the design and content of the finished work. For example, the space available for display of any detailed information now depends not only on the overall size of the whole map but on the area on that map within which the information could be placed and still be reasonably representative of its true position. With statistical maps this important element of position forces one to work within rather finer limits than with statistical diagrams, but fortunately a very wide range of techniques is available to help to overcome this problem. These range from very simple ones to those which are precise almost to the point of pedantry; let us consider a very simple type first.

NON-QUANTITATIVE STATISTICAL MAPS

No statistical map could be simpler in its design than the non-quantitative variety. Its ambition seems equally simple—namely, to mark in the places or areas where any features of interest occur, without need to differentiate according to size or importance if any feature occurs more than once.

Because of the very generalised and non-quantitative nature of its information this is a very easy type of map to construct and one frequently met with in atlases and text-books. In its non-quantitative nature, however, also lies its weakness for, as will be seen later in this chapter, the quantitative aspect of various occurrences is often regarded as of sufficient importance to warrant the introduction of many very detailed methods to represent it on statistical maps.

Ironically enough, despite this obvious criticism, non-quantitative maps are often among the most successful statistical devices. Their great merit lies in their ability to *summarise* a situation. Being free from any specific code of representation they can cut away ruthlessly all confusing detail and leave only the fundamental items for the observer to notice.

Much depends here on the care exercised in their preparation. If the information finally presented has been derived by reducing a great deal of material to manageable proportions then they may in fact be among the most discriminating and sophisticated of statistical maps; if, on the other hand, they plot anything and everything they may be almost useless and even downright misleading. Should more information be available than is needed, it may even be possible to overcome the worst aspects of their non-quantitative nature by crudely categorising any items plotted, as, for example, major and minor occurrences, large, medium or small examples, and so on. This has been done in Fig. 12 where very detailed information was available from the 'Atlas över Sverige'.

Further situations in which the non-quantitative map has advantages arise where the information to be plotted is in rather variable form (e.g. given in several different units which are not easily interconvertible) of varied reliability or of varied and not strictly comparable nature; e.g. in Fig. 12 it would be almost impossible, except in terms of value, to find any way of making quantitative comparisons between, say, ship-building and textiles, however detailed a method had been used.

QUANTITATIVE METHODS

Despite what has just been said in favour of the non-quantitative statistical map, aspects of quantity are often most important in statistical mapping, particularly if the topic under consideration is a relatively simple distribution of only one or two items. The very word 'statistical' implies some assessment of quantity and it is the aim of most published statistics to present this quantitative information to the user in the most convenient manner, and of most statistical cartographers to represent this by means of visually appreciable methods. It cannot be denied that in both cases the results sometimes fail lamentably.

To a certain extent the form in which the actual statistical information is given may well influence the techniques which can be used and the design of the resultant map, for there are three basic types of quantitative statistical distributions with rather different techniques to suit each. These three main types, as indicated in Fig. 2, are those in which quantities occur (1) at a

Fig. 12. A Non-Quantitative Statistical Map—Main Industrial Areas in Sweden (after Bergsten).

series of points, (2) contained within given areas and (3) along a series of lines. Let us consider them in that order.

QUANTITIES DISTRIBUTED AT A SERIES OF POINTS

Of all three basic types of distribution this one probably causes least complications; there is, for example, no possible doubt as to the location on the map at which a quantitative symbol should be placed. Unfortunately, statistics relating to this kind of distribution are not so common as is normally imagined. The great majority of published statistics relate in fact to *areas* and many which at first sight may seem not to do so, e.g. information about a particular town, will usually be found to refer to an administrative area centred on that town. Fortunately, the scale of the base map can help in some of these cases and a unit which would have to be treated as an area at a scale of 1 in. to a mile can often be regarded as a point on a scale of, say, 1:500,000.

Minor difficulties such as this excepted, the only important problem is to devise a suitable form of proportional symbol which can successfully represent the quantities concerned where they occur. If possible the symbol should be bold, compact and visually appreciable and a variety of solutions have been suggested.

REPEATED SYMBOLS

One of the simplest of these is the repeated symbol. This can be either of the simple or geometric kind, as in Fig. 13A, or of a pictorial or descriptive nature. Thus a given unit of population or labour force might be represented by a diagrammatically drawn human figure, so many million gallons of oil production by a drawing of a derrick or barrel, and so on, with quantities less than the unit chosen being shown by only partially completed symbols.

Fig. 13. Goods unloaded at French Ports in 1958, shown by—(*a*) *Fig. 13A.* Repeated Unit Symbols. (*b*) *Fig. 13B.* Proportional Bars. *Source:* Institut National de la Statistique et des Études Économique, *Annuaire Statistique de la France, 1959,* Paris, 1959.

The great appeal of the method lies in its simplicity—quantities can easily be deduced by counting symbols and the representative nature of the pictorial device makes its message easily understood, even by quite young children. Even so, the method has its difficulties. The pictorial type of symbol may be cumbersome and certainly is often tedious to draw, although geometric ones as in Fig. 13A are simpler and fit into smaller space; rather more troublesome is the nature of the symbol, which is in effect a linear one made up of several units. This makes large quantities difficult to handle and counting the symbols only remains practicable as long as their number is fairly small. A solution to this last difficulty is to introduce a second size of symbol representing a larger quantity, so that the number of units involved becomes much reduced; values represented by this means have the great advantage that they can be 'read back' from the map or diagram quickly and with a fair degree of accuracy.

Though the dot map (the counterpart of this method for use with statistics relating to areas) is widely used, repeated symbols *for point values* are not particularly common, perhaps because of the considerable amount of space which is occupied by a compound symbol of this kind with spaces between each unit. A symbol composed of a single unit is inevitably more compact and easier to draw and it is devices of this kind, rather than repeated symbols, which are often used for quantitative maps of point values. Space is very often at a premium on a complicated statistical map and, furthermore, where congestion occurs, symbols 'in bits and pieces' are apt to become confused with their neighbours.

PROPORTIONAL BARS

A compact analogy of the repeated symbols used in Fig. 13A is the proportional bar of the kind shown in Fig. 13B. We have already met the bar in some of its varied forms twice before and the idea here is still basically the same. The bars can be of any convenient width, i.e. broad enough to give a suitably solid symbol but not so broad that they get into one another's way, and can be placed either vertically or horizontally with one end close to the point where the quantity is located.

The bars are simple to draw, flexible to arrange in congested areas and, because of the simple linear form, easy to estimate visually, either unaided or with the help of some sort of scale which can easily be added, as in Fig. 13B. Even so the device is not particularly successful and is in consequence not widely used. One great defect is that the linear nature of the symbol makes it very difficult to accommodate a range of quantities of any great extent. A quantity 100 times larger than another needs a bar 100 times as long and this leads either to bars which are so small that they are almost invisible or so long that they have to be broken up into sections which can be 'stacked', e.g. the bars for Le Havre and Marseilles on Fig. 13B. Rather more pertinent an objection, however, is the fact that the bar has little sense of place; particularly as its size increases the visual 'weight' of the bar becomes more and more detached from the actual locality it is supposed to symbolise and the message of the map becomes rather vague from a distributional point of view.

The proportional bar is, perhaps, most successful where one end relates to some obvious feature, such as a coastline, so that it is easy to see which end matters and which locality is indicated. Certainly the device is more widely used for representing port traffic than almost any other kind of activity and where the bars can be drawn in extensive areas of sea the extreme length is not so marked an inconvenience.

PROPORTIONAL CIRCLES

The difficulties of the linear scale of values associated with the proportional bar can easily be overcome by introducing a second dimension and producing symbols whose *area* will be proportional to the quantity represented. Circles and squares are the obvious choice and, of the two, circles, which are much easier to draw, are far more frequently encountered. The device has already been met with in principle in discussing pie graphs, and instructions for drawing a series of circles with areas proportional to a given range of numbers will be found under that heading.

The advantages of introducing area instead of length are immediately apparent. Since the area of the figures is proportional to the *square* of the radius or length of side, a symbol 100 times the amount of another need now have a square or circle only 10 times as a large and a much greater range of values can be represented by legible symbols. On the other hand the bulk of the symbols may be troublesome. Even in congested localities it is not difficult to make room for another bar, but a proportional square or circle is not so easily fitted in and overlapping is frequently the only possible solution. Fig. 14A, which shows daily passenger traffic at stations in West Middlesex, illustrates a series of statistics where both the values to be represented and the locations of those values almost preclude the possibility of avoiding overlap. Overlap is not necessarily to be deplored, however, for congestion immediately attracts the eye and may be very useful in emphasising important areas in the distribution.

It is usual to add to maps of this kind a scale, either of diameters or of examples of typical values.

PROPORTIONAL SPHERES AND CUBES

The possibility of dealing more easily with extended ranges of values does not end with the introduction of a second dimension. A third dimension exists and, not surprisingly, cartographers have thought of using it to produce symbols whose *volume* would be proportional to the quantity they represent. The result is the proportional spheres or, much more rarely, cubes which are occasionally to be seen in statistical mapping.

Unlike the square or circle the sphere and cube bring rather more disadvantages than advantages in their train. Their great merit lies in the fact that within a given range of symbol size a very much wider range of values can be accommodated. The volume of these symbols is proportional to the *cube* of their radius or length of side and a symbol 10 times larger than another will now represent a value 10^3, i.e. 1,000 times greater, but here the advantages end. Mathematically correct though this relationship may be the ability of most people to translate its visual representation is very limited indeed and the implications that a symbol 10 times bigger than another represents a 1,000-fold increase are frequently not realised, even with a scale of values to help. This is another example of sticking too rigidly to mathematics and forgetting the limitations of the observer; estimation from bars is easy, from squares and circles more difficult, but from spheres and cubes almost impossible so far as the ordinary person is concerned—a point which will be elaborated further in Chapter 4.

Other difficulties with this method arise from the actual drawing of the symbols, which is far from easy. Cubes, though rarely used, can be represented without too much difficulty if they are drawn isometrically; spheres are more difficult and are usually drawn in one of two conventions, either as 'globes' with a crude graticule of meridians and parallels or as 'illuminated billiard balls' with a highlight near the top of the ball. The spheres in Fig. 14C are drawn in this second manner and in both styles the detail is used to secure a convincing three-dimensional effect. Successful achievement of this by either method is tedious and sometimes produces the disconcerting effect of causing the symbol to appear 'floating' above the map and detached from its locality, whilst unsuccessful results look flat and destroy the visual theory behind the method.

Fig. 14C shows an example of the use of proportional spheres to plot the same data as Fig. 14A. As so often happens the location of the individual values means that it is still impossible to avoid overlap, even with the possibility of dealing with larger numbers more compactly, and the labour involved in drawing the map was very considerable. On the whole the problems of extended ranges are perhaps best tackled by other means than the introduction of complicated mathematical relationships. Chapter 4 gives some possible lines of approach, but other techniques too can be called in to help.

A RANGE OF GRADUATED SYMBOLS

One such technique is the use of a range of graduated symbols, each symbol representing a specific group of values, the symbols increasing convincingly in size as the quantities they represent get larger. If simple circular symbols are used it is possible to maintain some sort of mathematical relationship by making them proportional in size to the mean or median value of the quantities in the group, thus producing a 'proportional circles map' with a much reduced variety of symbols, but, it is seriously open to question whether this preoccupation with mathematical accuracy is really worth all the trouble it is likely to cause. As Chapter 4 will show, it has only limited success visually, and a result no more misleading, much more positive and much easier to draw can be produced by using a well-devised range of graduated symbols (of circular or any other shape) as has been done in Fig. 14B.

In West Middlesex the number of passengers using the stations each day varied from 40 at Colnbrook to 31,4000 at Golders Green, but all values within this range were represented by a series of eight graduated symbols. The size of these symbols is, of course, quite arbitrary, but was conditioned by such obvious factors as the need for the largest symbols, which represented very large numbers indeed, to be dominant visually, whether this caused overlapping or not; even if strict mathematical relationships are not maintained it would be equally foolish to ignore them completely.

It is also important, since everything has been grouped into categories, that the symbols used for each should be distinct and recognisable on sight. This is very frequently ignored on maps using this device so that it becomes impossible to distinguish quickly one kind of symbol from another, e.g. where a range of, say, ten graduated circles, each only slightly larger than the next, is employed. Fig. 14B attempts to avoid this by achieving graduation through an intermediate type of symbol, the 3rd, 5th and 7th symbols in the range being

KEY

THE DAILY NUMBER OF PASSENGERS AT EACH STATION

MAP A (SAMPLE VALUES)	MAP B	MAP C (SAMPLE VALUES)
100 OR LESS	0 TO 600	200 OR LESS
300	800 " 2,400	700
1,000	2,500 " 3,700	2,000
3,000	3,900 " 7,100	5,000
7,000	7,400 " 10,900	10,000
15,000	11,400 " 15,000	20,000
	16,200 " 21,400	
30,000	24,100 " 31,400	30,000

"UNDERGROUND" LINES (MAP B) ⟵⟶

ROUTES TO CENTRAL LONDON ⟶

Fig. 14. Passenger Traffic at Stations in West Middlesex in 1951, shown by: (*a*) *Fig. 14A.* Proportional Circles. (*b*) *Fig. 14B.* A Range of Graduated Circular Symbols. (*c*) *Fig 14C.* Proportional Spheres. *Source:* County of Middlesex *Development Plan, 1951, Report of the Survey.*

made by adding to the preceding symbol an outer circle equal in diameter to the succeeding one, thereby achieving a transition which is gradual and visually distinct. This is only one way of making this distinction, however, and many other devices such as a notched or marked symbol could be used.

The gradual range of symbols has several easily recognised merits. It is easy to draw, avoids calculations and allows much wider freedom in accommodating the range of values; equally as important is the fact that, where a large number of quantities are represented, as in Fig. 14B, it makes appreciation of the total message of the map easier by sorting out for the observer one of the essential aspects of the distribution. Whereas with an infinite number of symbols the *difference* between quantities is always being stressed visually, *whether it matters or not*, a limited range of symbols stresses *the equally important similarities* which many of these quantities may share. Thus in Fig. 14A Hayes stands out as rather different from its neighbours, whereas Fig. 14B shows that, *in terms of the kinds of variations encountered in the area*, this difference is relatively unimportant.

The most important step in the use of this technique comes in deciding just where the divisions between the various groups are to be placed. The result is of great significance visually, for each symbol says, as it were, 'I represent something quite different and distinct from the other symbols in use here', and it is important that the groups and the breaks between them should as nearly as possible be meaningful ones in respect of the quantities concerned. The immediate choice of round numbers for the divisions between groups should be avoided, however tempting and labour-saving this may be, for this will result in quite arbitrary groups and may emphasise differences which do not really exist.

The only satisfactory way of subdividing any range of numbers is to draw a dispersal graph which, despite its imposing-sounding name, is the simplest of devices. It is usually drawn on a strip of graph paper, either horizontal or vertical, long enough to accommodate a scale which covers all the range of values. Each value in turn is plotted on this scale by either a dot or a line of unit length, any value which occurs more than once having a second dot or line added to the first, and so on. Where the range of values is very great it is usually just as satisfactory not to plot the individual values but to group them in tens or even hundreds. Fig. 15 shows two such dispersal graphs used in constructing Figs. 14B and 17. In the first of these the values were grouped and plotted in units of 100, i.e. 0-99, 100-199 and so on, whereas in the second, which was concerned with percentages, each value could be plotted to the nearest whole number. The resultant graph shows clusters or 'mounds' of dots and lines separated by 'hollows' or breaks of varying clarity, the clusters suggesting obvious groupings to use for a symbol and the largest breaks the most obvious places for the divisions between the groups. The total result defines, as satisfactorily as possible, a natural subdivision of the whole range of quantities.

As Fig. 15 shows, constructing a dispersal graph is not an infallible panacea for difficulties in subdividing a range. Natural breaks may be either few and indistinct or far more numerous than the number of symbols which can be used (a maximum of about 10 seems wise if visual distinction is to be maintained.). Fig. 15A, for example, shows fairly marked groups centred on 400, 1,700, 2,800 and 4,500, but poor definition between about 5,000 and 11,000. In cases such as these other considerations can be invoked, e.g. trying to ensure that each group does

Fig. 15. Two Dispersal Graphs. These two dispersal graphs indicate the spread of values for points or areas plotted on Fig. 14 (Fig. 15A) and Fig. 17 (Fig. 15B). *Source:* As Figs. 14 and 17.

not cover too wide a range of values or, where there is no good reason to the contrary, using round numbers which are easier for the map user to remember. In Fig. 15A the division is far from ideal; many of the categories cover an increase in value of 40% or more between the lowest and highest numbers, but this increase must of course be seen in proportion to the whole range of values which the map attempts to cover. In Fig. 15B the division is rather more clear cut and the natural groups which result show the folly of arbitrarily choosing round numbers as dividing points, particularly at the upper end of the range where 70, 80 and 90 would all cut quite well-defined natural groups into two portions.

QUANTITIES CONTAINED WITHIN GIVEN AREAS

Statistics showing quantities contained within given areas are perhaps more common than any other type, but unfortunately their use is attended by several difficulties of a general nature. Chapter 3 is concerned with elaborating some of the finer aspects of these difficulties, but their broader aspects can well be introduced here. Foremost amongst them is the knowledge that the statistics simply indicate that within a given boundary-line a certain number of items are to be found; just how these objects are arranged within that boundary-line is not indicated—the distribution may be even or alternatively extremely uneven, and if the area concerned happens to be a large one such as a national territory then variations of this kind may be very marked indeed. Further information may bring to light more detailed distributional knowledge, but it is often the case that the only secondary sources available, e.g. maps of various kinds, are non-quantitative and leave the cartographer the problem of either making his own subjective estimate or working with average values for the whole unit, though he may know these to be unrepresentative or misleading.

Problems of this kind are less troublesome if the areas used are small, but it may be difficult or impossible to obtain a map showing the boundaries of the smallest administrative units for which figures are given. Ward boundaries in urban areas of Britain are a good example of this elusive type of information and if one is working on a period, say a century ago, with several boundary changes intervening it may prove surprisingly difficult to establish the boundaries of much larger units than wards; published statistics rarely carry a map showing the boundaries of *all* the areas for which information is given and naturally the problem is much worse if the information is required for units outside one's own country.

Very frequently it is impossible to obtain entirely satisfactory solutions to general problems such as these which arise from statistics relating to areas, but the results need not be too disappointing. Provided always that one approaches maps of this kind with a reasonable awareness of the difficulties which these statistics bring and the limitations of the cruder methods relating to larger areas the various techniques described below have a most useful and necessary part to play in statistical representation.

DOT MAPS

Few ideas could be simpler than the principle underlying the dot map, and yet few statistical techniques raise more ancillary problems before they can be put into practice. In theory the dot map is nothing more than the repeated symbol, which we have already met, applied to areas and confined to only one type of symbol, the dot. If each dot represents so much or so many of a particular item a simple division sum will indicate how many dots will represent the quantity contained within a given area and these dots must then be placed within that area on the map.

This theoretical statement of the method is deceptively simple, for it has already introduced three unknowns, each of which can be varied and needs to be solved before mapping can begin; these are:

(1) How much or how many shall each dot represent?
(2) How big shall each dot be?
(3) Exactly how shall each dot be placed within the area?

A fourth problem, how shall each dot be drawn, could also be added.

The answer to the first of these problems must be suggested by the statistics themselves. Generally speaking, it is desirable to have at least two or three dots for each area so that within each area there is at least a crude pattern of dot distribution; it is with variations in this pattern from one area to the next that the message of the map begins. The great difficulty lies in finding a dot value which achieves a satisfactory compromise by producing this effect at the lower end of the range and yet does not demand an excessive number of dots for the larger quantities which will almost inevitably occur.

The second question is even more subtle and will to a great extent depend upon decisions just described and on methods available for drawing the dots. It should be remembered that, within the dot map, variations in the density of dots over the face of the map must be judged by changes in the ratio of solid dots to white background, and if this is to be successful as wide a variation as possible should be introduced into the amount of the 'black' dot component. A useful working rule is to try to arrange the number and size of the dots so that they will just begin to coalesce in the densest areas; this implies that since any area where no dots are needed will be 'white' the map will carry all variations from white to almost solid colour and the eye will have this wide variation to help in estimation. The point is well illustrated in Figs. 16A and B, where exactly the same distribution has been plotted twice, once with large dots and again with smaller dots. It is immediately apparent that in Fig. 16B it is much more difficult to judge variations in density, and the smaller amount of black on the map tends to reduce everything to a more even-looking distribution. In Fig. 16A the congestion produced by the bigger dot is a decided advantage, emphasising and attracting attention towards the areas of densest distribution.

One of the most difficult aspects of using larger dots lies in finding some satisfactory way of drawing them. The best method is undoubtedly to obtain a special pen nib which has the end rounded and bent at an angle to the rest of the nib so that each application produces one dot (see Fig. 39 (p. 105) for an illustration of such a pen). These are known as *dotting-pens* and come in a wide range of sizes; similar to these are pen nibs supplied for lettering but which have the rounded part bent at right angles to the rest of the nib. These also produce a dot if merely applied to the paper without movement. The dots in Fig. 16A were drawn with one of the larger pens supplied for use with 'UNO' stencils. These again form a dot if merely touched to the paper, but the larger pens are very free-flowing and will 'blob' unless only a very small quantity of ink is placed in the reservoir; if this does not cure the trouble, it will help to touch the point on blotting paper before each application.

Other methods which can be used if these technical aids are not available are stick-printing of dots, sticking punched dots on to the map or punching out holes in the map which is then placed over a backing sheet. The best and fullest account of the technicalities of these other methods will be found in Birch, *Maps*[1], but they will not be elaborated further here. The layman will probably find one or another of the three types of pen described above more easily obtainable and quicker in action, while the experienced draughtsman will already have established his preferences. The use of a springbow compass for drawing *small* dots is not recommended to the inexperienced draughtsman, for it will be found difficult to produce consistent, circular results. If crayon or pencil techniques are being used a useful, easy and quick way of drawing large dots will be found by taking a piece of thin card, punching out several holes with an ordinary filing punch and using these as a stencil by first 'drawing round' the hole and then filling in whilst the card is still in position. Holes wear relatively quickly, but new ones can easily be added to replace them.

In at least one type of map the problem of dot size can sometimes be eliminated. If the dot represents an *areal* quantity then it can of course be made true to scale and the map will give a realistic impression of the amount of land actually occupied by the feature under discussion. The calculations involved are not difficult. Determine beforehand (a) the scale of the base map, expressed as so many miles to 1 in.—call this quantity S and (b) the value in acres which one dot shall represent—call this quantity D. Then to find the radius (R) in inches of such a dot on a map of this scale a formula can be derived as follows:

[1] T. W. Birch, *Maps—Topographical and Statistical* (Chapter 22), Oxford, 1949.

Fig. 16. Southern Part of the State of Michigan, Area of Land in Farms, 1954, shown by: (*a*) *Figs. 16A and 16B.* Dots, working from a basis of constituent counties. (*b*) *Fig. 16C.* Proportional Circles for each county. In Figs. 16A and 16B the information portrayed is identical except for the size of the dot used, illustrating the marked advantage of the larger dot in assessing variations in the distribution pattern. *Source:* U.S. Bureau of the Census, *1954 Census of Agriculture*, Washington, D.C., 1956.

47

1. The scale is S miles to one inch, therefore 1 sq. in. will represent S^2 square miles or $640S^2$ acres (there are 640 acres in a sq. mile).

2. By proportion, if $640S^2$ acres occupy 1 sq. in. on the map D acres, the dot value, will occupy $\dfrac{D}{640S^2}$ sq. in. This is the area of the dot.

3. $\pi R^2 = \dfrac{D}{640S^2}$ therefore $R = \sqrt{\dfrac{D}{640\pi S^2}}$

This can be rearranged as $\dfrac{\sqrt{D}}{S} \times \dfrac{1}{\sqrt{640\pi}}$ and since $\dfrac{1}{\sqrt{640\pi}} = \cdot 0223$, $R = \dfrac{\cdot 0223\sqrt{D}}{S}$

In metric measure, if S is in kilometres per centimetre and D is in hectares then R (in centimetres) $= \dfrac{\cdot 0564\sqrt{D}}{S}$

Once the value of R is calculated it would be reasonable to use any dot diameter which approximated to this quantity without reproducing it with mathematical accuracy.

It does not necessarily follow that where the dot symbol is used to represent areal quantities this procedure need always be followed. A great deal depends on just how much of the total surface the use under discussion actually occupies. In Fig. 16A the land in farms not surprisingly totals over 80% of the area of many counties in Michigan and therefore true areal representation will produce the desirable coalescence of dots which was mentioned earlier. On the other hand, had the map tried to show the distribution in the same state of, for example, orchard land, which will not occupy such a large area even in the most important fruit-growing districts, the result would have been too 'thin' and a dot 'larger than life' would have given a better result.

Whatever dot value and dot size are used it should be borne in mind that an area full of dots on the map will carry a psychological impression that on the ground the same area is full of whatever is being mapped, and in the same way too sparse a sprinkling of dots conveys an unmistakable impression of emptiness. Aspects such as this, which arise from decisions on dot size and value, may prompt some modifications to the general rule of trying to achieve coalescence in the denser areas if this would be quite out of keeping with reality.

The problem of placing the dots within the area is, if anything, more difficult to solve than those arising from the two variables so far discussed. Two fundamentally opposed solutions are possible within any given area: either (a) spread the dots evenly, or (b), if variations are known to occur within the area, attempt an uneven distribution of the dots so that they are as representative as possible of these variations. The latter is easily the best solution. The results will be more realistic and will exploit the one very important asset of the dot symbol—namely, its flexibility. Unfortunately, distribution of dots within areas on this basis will almost certainly call for a good deal of guesswork and subjective judgement and the results will vary in reliability depending on the cartographer's detailed knowledge of the topic which is being mapped and the number and nature of any sources which he may have to help him in his judgement. Help of one sort or another will frequently be available for this problem, but unfortunately it will often be qualitative rather than quantitative, so that whilst it may, for example, indicate firmly where *not* to place the dots it will give no strong positive guide as to numbers in those areas were dots are needed. Maps are among the commonest and most easily available aids of this kind: e.g. even a simple topographical map at a scale of 1 in. to a mile or 1:50,000 would assist in placing dots representing a population distribution by indicating where villages and hamlets were but not, of course, the detailed population of each unit; similarly it might help in plotting agricultural statistics by marking areas of marsh, moor, forest, towns and industry which would need to be left blank on the map. More specialised maps may be even more useful.

Subjective placing of dots in this way has been criticised as introducing into the dot map errors of personal judgement which cannot easily be checked, and whilst this cannot be denied it seems reasonable to point out that the errors involved need be no more misleading than those which are visually unobtrusive but so well known to be present when the dots are spread evenly; moreover, a person constructing a dot map must surely have some additional knowledge of its subject matter beyond the bare statistics and his errors will at least be associated with the intention of taking a step in the direction of establishing the true distribution.

Spreading the dots evenly throughout an area overcomes these difficulties, but often produces a misleading 'average' picture. Used in this manner dots become a kind of infinitely variable shading indicating density within the area but with the major disadvantage, in comparison with other methods which will be described shortly, that they can give no direct indication of this density themselves nor is it easy to add to the map a suitably graduated scale against which comparisons can be made. It is seriously open to consideration whether shading or proportional shading of areas would not be more effective a method than dots spread evenly. Furthermore, it is not easy to achieve an even distribution of a given number of dots within an area and it is always advisable to plot them in pencil first and check for a satisfactory result before inking in. If small numbers of dots are required their locations are easily 'planned' in advance, but if larger numbers are needed the best method seems to be to begin by making an open, even distribution of a few dots and then gradually filling in the spaces, working continually over the whole area all the time. Starting at one end and hoping that the correct distribution has been hit upon so that one will just run out of dots by the time the other end is reached will rarely give satisfactory results.

It is a bad policy, too, to fight shy of placing dots near the boundary line of an area. The centre of the dot is its true location and dots can and should overlap boundary lines if this is necessary. Very often these boundaries are erased from the finished map and unless this precaution is observed the former position of boundary lines will often stand out as empty lines on the map.

In spite of all these difficulties the dot map has been widely used. Its basic idea is attractively simple, no other method relating to areas has the same flexibility and it has a particular appeal from the discontinuous nature of the dot symbols which portray satisfactorily many distributions which are themselves discontinuous in reality, e.g. land under various crops. On the other hand, of all the methods described in this book it is the least positive in its quantitative message, for though the individual dot is quantitative enough one soon wishes to make comparisons of quantities in areas which contain tens or hundreds of dots and this is quite impracticable. The dot map, in effect, shows variations in distribution admirably, but portrays quantities very weakly, so that it is best used in showing distributions which are patchy and where marked variations occur. Thus Fig. 16A is able to show well both the patchy distribution of land in farms in the northern half of the peninsula and also the contrast this provides with the southern portion of the state. If the distribution is a fairly even one with variations which are *relatively small but nevertheless important* the dot map will not be a very suitable method to use. The apparently even distribution of land in farms which Fig. 16B shows in the south-west corner of Michigan, for example, can be contrasted with the manner in which certain differences are clearly picked out where the same information is shown by shading on Fig. 17B (p. 53).

It has also been demonstrated that with dot maps impressions of density of dots in any small area on the map may be markedly influenced by the number and arrangement of the dots which surround that area, but this seems rather an academic point in view of the general weaknesses in legibility, in this and many other methods, which will be described in Chapter 4.

SHADING MAPS[1]

Shading techniques present, on the whole, simpler and cruder methods of portraying statistics relating to areas than do dot maps. Both of these characteristics derive from the fact that shading methods *presuppose uniform distribution of the quantity throughout the area*, aspects of quantity and area, for example, being combined by calculating the *average density* of the distribution within the area and representing this density on the map by some form of shading applied to the whole area.

It cannot be stressed too heavily that with shading techniques *the effect on quantities caused by the varying sizes of the areas used must not be allowed to intrude*. The most usual way of overcoming this difficulty is to express quantities as a *density* per square kilometre, acre, etc., or as some quantity which is entirely independent of area such as a *percentage, ratio or per capita figure. Straightforward numerical quantities should never be shown on shading maps.* The reasons for this are almost self-evident, but the author has found that students are persistently tempted into trying to show quantities in this way, frequently in an attempt to avoid the calculations necessary to turn quantities into densities. In a perfectly uniform distribution with two adjacent units, one twice as large in area as the other, the former will obviously contain twice as much of the feature being studied as will its smaller neighbour. If shading by *quantity* were applied, these two units would be sharply differentiated, whereas the distribution is uniform, one only containing a greater quantity by virtue of its greater size. A map made in this way would reflect variations in the area of the units used and not, as was its intention, variations in the distributions of some particular feature.

Having expressed quantities for each area in some suitable form, some means must then

[1] Sometimes described as *choropleth* maps. It is unfortunate that the essentially simple techniques of statistical cartography have been given a variety of complicated, confusing and not-yet-standardised names of pseudo-Greek origin. With the exception of the term *isoline* (see later) these terms are deliberately omitted from this book. It is the author's opinion that they suggest a *mystique* where none exists and tend to induce a rigid rather than a flexible approach to the various techniques.

be found for showing these on the map. The most widely used method is to divide the range of values into suitable groups and distinguish all values falling within that group by a particular type of shading. The problem is very similar to that which was encountered earlier in devising a range of graduated symbols and it needs to be approached in a similar manner. The division into shading groups is important because, as with symbols, each shading type proclaims similarity within its boundaries and distinctiveness from areas beyond its limits; a dispersal graph is the only really satisfactory way of ascertaining the most suitable places for these divisions in a wide range of numbers.

The divisions established, a suitable range of shading must be devised. An infinite number of variations is possible here, but certain general rules can be applied. The most important is that the shading, in its increasing density of tone, should have a visual resemblance to the kind of numerical increase which it represents. An ideal solution would be to control the density of the shading (i.e. the black-white ratio) mathematically, so that shading representing densities twice as great as those elsewhere would be twice as dark in tone. This could easily be done mechanically with prepared dots and stipples and also by various hand methods which will be described later, but the fact that one type of shading usually represents a group of values, which would have to be replaced by their mean or median, weakens the apparent exactitude of the method, and experiments have shown that, unfortunately, a range of shading which increases evenly in density from white to black does not in fact *appear* to do so to the eye.

In practice there is no need to stick slavishly to mathematics; a reasonably devised increase in intensity will serve most purposes and it is much more important that each type of shading should be distinctive enough to be recognisable on sight. This places a limit on the number of divisions that can be used, although much will depend on whether colour or black and white only is available. Whichever is the case, a maximum of eight or ten types seems suitable in practice. More variations than this, even where each is suitably distinct, gives the eye rather too much detail to look at although a greater number might be justified if it were intended that the map should be used as a statistical 'quarry' rather than as a picture of a situation.

As with dots, the overall impression of variations in shading is important. A range of shading which has very little gradation in intensity will produce a psychological impression that the values it represents show a similarly small range of variations, even though several subdivisions may be distinguished; a wide range of shading tone gives the converse effect and any such psychological impression should not be at variance with the figures.

It is not essential that the two extremes of any range of shading should be 'white' and solid colour. Quite apart from the psychological implications of these two particular tones—the one implying emptiness, the other extreme plenty—they are particularly strong visually, being more easily recognisable than the other types of shading and tending to dominate the map. This may or may not be a satisfactory state of affairs. Frequently it is important that extreme values *should* be emphasised, but once again the shading should be matched up with the figures and the impression it is required to produce.

If colours are available it is usually advisable to limit the number to two or three and build up variety by using several tones in each colour rather than several colours. Once again the balance is a delicate one. It is not at all easy visually to identify at first glance any one of say six shades of yellow, and in this case it would be better to use three yellows and pass on into three shades of brown or orange; the transition from yellow to orange or brown will need making with care if a gradual series is being attempted, but could be kept quite striking if this point in the series marked a major break. Where several colours are used it is usual to pass from one to another in spectrum order, i.e. red, orange, yellow, green, blue, indigo and violet, though it will be found better to keep the latter half of this sequence for negative values. Between yellow and green there is often a more marked colour break than in the rest of the sequence and the arrangement accords well with the established psychological properties of colour, red being a dominant colour, violet a recessive one.

In practice it is naturally easier to obtain suitable tones by using colours which can be mixed with one another to produce transitions. Water colours and poster colours come off best here whilst media which have 'fixed' colours, such as crayons or bottles of coloured inks used without mixing, make it difficult to achieve the required gradation of tone.

If black and white alone are used shading can either be applied by hand or by the use of ready-printed thin adhesive cellulose sheets which can be cut to the required shape and applied to the map. This latter method is becoming very widely used and a surprising variety of shading, stipples and other patterns and devices are available.[1] Unfortunately for the layman it is rather expensive, tedious if the areas are many and small or with irregular boundaries and the sheets are not widely stocked, often having to be obtained to order. The result, however, is very neat and 'professional' in appearance. As an alternative, quite satis-factory results can be obtained by hand, building up patterns from lines and dots. As with dot maps it should be remembered that it is the ratio of black to white which gives the impression of intensity and this should be varied as much as possible, e.g. by *thickening* lines as well as by adding more to the pattern. To achieve an even result it is best to place the map on a tracing table over a sheet of graph paper which will act as a guide for the spacing of the lines or dots; rows of dots are more successfully drawn if made with the pen touching a bevelled straight-edge every time it is applied to the paper.

Several of these points are illustrated in Figs. 17A and B which indicate the percentage of land in farms in counties in part of the State of Michigan. The juxtaposition of Figs. 17A and B emphasises the rather different impressions which are produced when, still using the same number and types of shading, different values are chosen for the limits of the shading types. In Fig. 17A the values used were those taken from the 'Land in Farms' map for the whole of the U.S.A. produced by the Bureau of the Census. Though these may be very suitable for dealing with the whole country, and may have to be used if other states were to be mapped in a comparable way, they are *not* suitable for an isolated map of the distribution in the State of Michigan alone. In Fig. 15B, where the distribution of values has already been analysed, it was seen that 80 and 90, for example, *bisect* natural groups and the dispersal graph suggests the much more logical subdivision used in Fig. 17B. Fig. 17B also shows that where the map does not form part of a series there is no need for the key to be numbered continuously; it is more indicative of the actual state of affairs if the range of each group is given as lying between existing maximum and minimum values, rather than 'theoretical' ones as in Fig. 17A.

[1] For example those sold under the trade name of *Zip-a-tone*.

Fig. 17. Southern Part of the State of Michigan, Percentage of Land in Farms, 1954, shown by: (a) *Figs. 17A and 17B.* Normal shading techniques. (b) *Fig. 17C.* Normal shading techniques modified by 'rounding off' boundaries of constituent areas. (c) *Figs. 17D and 17E.* Isolines. (d) *Fig. 17F.* Proportional shading. Since all six sections derive from the same basic information this figure gives an opportunity to compare the effect of using different methods for the presentation of a single piece of material. The effect of variations *within* each method can be seen by comparing Fig. 17A with 17B and 17C with 17D; these show the different impressions of distribution which can be produced simply by varying the limiting values of the different types of shading which are employed. *Source:* U.S. Bureau of the Census, *1954 Census of Agriculture,* Washington, D.C., 1956.

The seven shading types used in Figs. 17A and B were based on simple, hand-applied line and dot patterns with rather a marked step in visual intensity between the third and fourth. This helps particularly to emphasise the contrasts between the northern and southern parts of the peninsula in Fig. 17B, but this effect is almost lost in Fig. 17A where the line patterns begin at a lower value.

The shading map has one great disadvantage which we have already touched upon— namely, the presupposition that density over a whole area is uniform. This problem is similar to that which was encountered when the distribution of dots within areas was being discussed and it can be resolved in the same way, by making some sort of subjective assessment of the variations which probably exist. J. K. Wright has suggested such a method where one has statistics for a unit which is known to contain two quite different types of territory.[1] Briefly described, the procedure involves first delineating these subdivisions on the map and then making a reasoned guess at the density which exists in one of them. This can be done particularly by comparison with areas of a similar type which may form complete units and for which typical density values would therefore be known. If such a density is then supposed in one subdivision whose area can be measured, the total quantity contained in that subdivision can be calculated (area × density) and the result subtracted from the total quantity for the whole unit; this will yield the quantity in the other subdivision for which the area and then the density can be calculated. Once again, although the method involves an element of personal judgement, the results, when made by a well-informed person, are not likely to be more misleading than the unadjusted values. As an example of an area where this kind of calculation is justified there can be quoted the Urban District of Pickering in North Yorkshire, which, though essentially centred round a small market town on the edge of the Vale of Pickering, is extremely elongated, stretching up in a tongue nine miles long almost to the crest of the North York Moors, and including in its northern end a considerable area of hamlets, scattered farms and moorland. It would be misleading to colour in over the whole of such an area urban characteristics such as population density which apply to only part of it. Fortunately, adjacent to this northern portion there are several entire rural parishes which occupy similar territory, and whose densities of population would be a useful guide in estimating a figure for this northern area.

A further disadvantage of shading maps is that boundaries assume a degree of significance out of all proportion to their true importance so far as a particular distribution is concerned. Abrupt changes of shading which occur at boundary lines hardly ever have any counterpart in reality, and equally stupidly this marked break has to follow every minor inflection and promontory of the boundary itself; detached portions of units are a particular inconvenience here though they can sometimes be dealt with in the manner described above. In matters such as this, the inflexible shading techniques show up poorly against the discontinuous patterns made by dots, which effect rather less noticeably abrupt transitions, but to some extent this disadvantage can be partially overcome simply by smoothing and rounding off the shapes which would result if the boundaries were exactly reproduced. Fig. 17C provides an example of this with the values which were used in Fig. 17B treated in this way.

[1] J. K. Wright, 'A Method of Mapping Densities of Population with Cape Cod as an Example' *Geographical Review*, vol. 26, New York, 1936.

In Figs. 17A and B the rectangularity of administrative units, though odd to European eyes, produces blocks of shading of reasonable shape so long as units do not occur diagonally when an odd-looking pattern results; it seems reasonable to smooth this off into a diagonal band or, for example, to turn a cross shape into a circular one of rather smaller dimensions.

PROPORTIONAL SHADING

Shading techniques, like dot maps, are widely used despite their disadvantages. Their particular asset is the positive nature of their message, clearly placing the quantity being represented within a given range of values, and so far this is as much as we have expected of them. It is possible, however, to devise shading techniques which will not merely place a value within a range but actually represent it, 'true to scale' as it were. This possibility has already been touched upon in considering mechanical shading patterns, but no complete range of these is likely to be produced as a commerial proposition. Hand techniques, however, can provide a suitable equivalent, and two ways have been suggested.

The first of these is more akin to mechanical methods, but tedious to draw. It requires bands of a convenient width, say 1 in., to be ruled horizontally across the map, these bands being then filled in with a number of horizontal lines according to a scale of one line for a particular number of items. An example will make the point clear. Let us suppose that a map is being prepared to show the density per square mile of workers in agriculture, and that the values to be plotted range from 200 to 20: a scale of one line for every ten workers might be decided upon. Twenty lines would then have to be inserted between each pair of horizontal lines in the area where the density of 200 occurred but only 2 where the density was 20. This would involve dividing the space between the main horizontal lines into 20 equal parts in one case, 2 in the other, 17 if the density was 170 and so on, each density being brought to the nearest ten before work commenced. The tedium arises from repeating this process of division for say sixty different areas. The actual process of division is not in itself difficult and several methods are available, whilst any densities which are repeated can be easily drawn in by 'transferring' the spacing from the first example.

Although the intensity of the lines is indeed proportional to the quantity represented, it is not easy to make comparisons from one area to another; and in effect the discontinuous horizontal lines which make up this type of shading have become as incomparable one with another as the discontinuous dot pattern on the dot map. A scale showing typical values is usually added beside such a map to help this comparison.

The author has found that a second method, rather easier to draw, is also more successful. As before, this needs bands ruling across the map, but in this case they need not be horizontal and they should be of a width of rather more (usually the next convenient round number) than the largest quantity to be represented; at right angles to these is drawn a line along which a scale of values in between the bands can be measured. As an example, if the largest value to be shown was 231 bands 250 units wide would be a suitable choice; in Fig. 17F where the highest value was 92 the bands were 100 units wide, the actual physical width being $\frac{1}{2}$ in. on the original drawing so that $\frac{1}{200}$th of an inch represented 1 unit on the scale line. Any value occurring within a given area can be represented by measuring up from the base of *each* band crossing the area a distance equivalent to that quantity measured on the scale line; a line is then ruled through this point parallel to the base of the band and the area between these two lines shaded in solid colour. A glance at Fig. 17F will make this quite clear, e.g. where the density was 86, a distance of ·43 in. was measured above each base line, producing a black band ·43 in. wide alternating with a white one ·07 in. wide across all areas where this value occurs. It should be noticed that not only base lines passing through an area but those passing close to the boundary must be considered as well, for a large quantity based on these may well bring the solid colour within the boundaries of the area although in this case filling-in extends only to the boundary and not to the base line.

The method is not difficult to use, but one or two points need some consideration. Foremost amongst these is the width of the bands which in turn will be affected by the size of the units for which values are given. It is desirable that the width should not be greater than the height of the smallest unit, although smaller band-widths involve more work and less easily made measurements along the scale line. A compromise may have to be made and it may be quite satisfactory to arrange the bands so that the smallest areas lie astride two bands where they cannot occupy a whole one; alternatively, tilting the bands may allow them to take advantage of some more favourable dimension in the smaller units. It is often helpful to rule the bands out first on tracing paper which can be juggled about over the map to find the most favourable position.

The result produced by this technique is a map which often has quite wide variation in the black-white ratio and a black component proportional to the quantity represented. Comparisons of value from one unit to another can easily be made, particularly between adjacent areas, by comparing the heights of the black bands in each case; a scale is easily added (see Fig. 17F) and although boundary lines are not eliminated, the absence of continuous colour means that their effect is more broken up and less obtrusive. A defect of the method is that the scale of shading is a linear one and, as such, may give difficulty in dealing with extended ranges of values.

Fig. 17F shows an example of a map prepared by this method, and it is interesting to contrast the picture it presents with the various impressions deriving from Figs. 17A to E. It offers, among other things, the first attempt to show the obvious contrast between the northern and southern halves of the peninsula in its true proportions.

ISOLINE MAPS

The 'unreal' effect which boundary lines produce on shading maps remains a major disadvantage. Smoothing off these boundaries may help (see Fig. 17C), but will not remove the problem of abrupt transition in values at a particular line. The isoline technique offers one way of overcoming both these disadvantages. As with shading techniques, it too starts out with an average density or similarly expressed value for each unit but regards this value as being *typical of* rather than *confined exactly* to the area under consideration. Each quantity is plotted on the map within its area as a 'spot-height' value and in between the 'spot-heights' 'contours' are drawn to show the trends of the figures. Between the 'contours' layer colouring or shading can be added for further emphasis. The analogy with layer-coloured relief maps is very strong, but should not be pursued too rigorously.

The method involves the solution of three main problems: (1) placing the spot-heights,

(2) deciding on suitable values for the contours and (3) drawing in the contours. The first of these is not particularly difficult; an obvious solution is to place the spot-height in the geographical centre of the unit, but if more detailed information of distribution within the area is known it will be found more satisfactory to attempt to place it at the 'centre-of-gravity' of the unit, much nearer to any local areas of particularly dense distribution. The second of these is an old problem in new guise. The values selected for the contours perform the same function here as those which divide different kinds of shading in a shading map, and they should therefore be chosen with the same degree of care, preferably by the use of a dispersal graph.

It is the last of these three problems which presents the cartographer with the more difficult situations so far as this method is concerned, although the basic principle is quite elementary. 'Contours', or as they are termed in this case *isolines* (*anglice* lines of equal value), which occur between any two adjacent spot-heights are fixed by drawing a straight line between the two points and spacing the isolines along this line proportionately to the difference between their value and that of the spot-heights. Thus if two isolines for 55 and 68 have to be drawn between a pair of values of 42 and 89 they will cut this line at points $13/47$ and $26/47$ of the total distance between the points measured from the lower value. In practice these distances are almost always judged by eye and in the above example estimates of just over $\frac{1}{4}$ and $\frac{1}{2}$ would suffice.

Calculations such as this establish points through which isolines should pass and the isolines themselves can be drawn in by joining up all established points relating to a particular value, but the process is not always so simple as it sounds. Common sense will often suggest some modification to the pattern which would derive simply by following the method described above for this has one major weakness: it presupposes that between any pair of spot-heights there will be found only intermediate values and never anything larger or smaller than either of them. To return to the relief analogy, it discounts the theory that either a marked ridge or valley could intervene between any pair of spot-heights. Rather unlikely looking results may be obtained if this idea is too strictly adhered to, the most usual characteristics being very elongated tongues or valleys, stretching out of or into areas of high values solely to 'catch' an isolated high or low value; a more sensible approach, treating these points as isolated 'knolls' or 'hollows', will produce much simpler isoline patterns.

Even when simple modifications of this kind are observed there is still room for a good deal of personal judgement in deciding just how and where isolines should be drawn, and two cartographers working from the same distribution of values will not necessarily produce identical results using this technique. Detailed knowledge of finer aspects of the distribution on the ground should always be used (where possible) as an additional aid in drawing the isolines and may suggest modifications to the basic proportional spacing, such as closer bunching for sharp transitions or added promontories and embayments not supported by any actual values.

The repeated reference to topographical terms in a description of this technique is almost inevitable in view of its noticeable analogy to relief maps, but it should be noted that major differences *in principle and practice* may have to be accepted if the best results are to be obtained. The essential feature of contoured maps drawn from spot heights of known value is that it is certain that between the spot heights *somewhere* there must occur places which exhibit every intermediate value, even though several of these may coincide in a cliff or crag. Thus between spot heights of 60 ft. and 100 ft. there must be heights of 61 ft., 62 ft., 85 ft., 90 ft. and so on. In a few cases where statistics are being represented by an isoline technique, a similar kind of distribution can be assumed. The most obvious group-example is climatic statistics for such quantities as temperature, pressure, rainfall or humidity. In these cases we are dealing with natural processes capable of infinite variation in which changes, though they may be quite sharp, cannot be abrupt; once again between places with 60 in. and 100 in. of rainfall there must be somewhere with 61 in., 62 in. and so on. When man-made distributions are being considered this kind of gradation need not follow, and changes may be entirely abrupt with no intermediate values at all. Thus an average population density of 2,000 per square mile for an urban unit and one of 200 for an adjacent rural area will not necessarily be separated by a zone of intermediate values. Although it is common to find the highest densities in urban units at the centre with lower densities as one goes outwards, this is only a general rule and the transition from 2,000 to 200 may literally occur on either side of a hedge—buildings on one side and fields on the other. An isoline map drawn to illustrate this distribution would normally include several intermediate isolines, admittedly very closely spaced, to mark this transition.

It can be seen that we have, in effect, two rather different classes of isoline maps, one corresponding to each situation. The first type attempts to use established values as a basis for interpolation all over the face of the map, the isolines helping estimation of values at places where statistics have not been recorded. This type of map aims at a high degree of accuracy.

In the second type the isolines' function is rather different; their essential purpose is to act as a visual guide to the interpretation of trends and tendencies which the plotted values indicate. The significance of intermediate values between these known points will depend very much on the kind of distribution being plotted and especially the degree to which the 'spot-heights' used reflect typical conditions in their area. Thus in the case of land in farms in the counties of Michigan (Figs. 17D and E (p. 53)) it does not seem unreasonable to assume that, throughout the southern portion of the area, the figure for the whole county is fairly representative of general conditions within that county. The author could find no overwhelming evidence of major 'unfarmed patches' of a size large enough to affect the result, small lakes and an occasional sizeable town being the only obvious, but relatively unimportant, exceptions. The picture which isolines present when drawn between spot-heights with this kind of distribution is probably fairly representative and the gradual transitions shown might be expected in reality. Unfortunately, conditions in the northern part of the peninsula are quite different; land in farms has a much more patchy distribution and the transition between farmed areas and large areas without farmed land seems fairly abrupt. The dot map in Fig. 16A gives some idea of this patchiness and average figures for a whole county have much less real meaning than further south so that the rather gradual changes which the isoline map indicates are unlikely to be found in practice and both higher and lower values than the ones shown might well be expected within many areas.

When showing man-made distributions with isoline maps of this second type, there seems no reason to pursue the analogy with relief too far, and with very patchy distributions it should be quite permissible to pass from a low value to a high value abruptly, without any need to include all intermediate isolines (see, for example, Fig. 42B (p. 122)). Such a modification of the method would be the most successful way of overcoming the hiatus between urban and rural densities, for example, with the added advantage that the change would take place at the most appropriate place and not, as with shading maps, at a fixed boundary line; on the other hand, unimportant abrupt changes of average density within a rural area can be satisfactorily smoothed out, using the normal isoline technique, giving a more flexible result than can be achieved with the ordinary shading map. With isoline maps of any type it is often useful to indicate all spot-height values from which the map was constructed so that the amount of interpolation which has been necessary can be seen at a glance.

Figs. 17D and E (p. 53) show two examples of the data used in Figs. 17A and B redrawn by this method. The effect of choosing different isoline values is clearly apparent, but the differential result here is due more to the various layer-colourings being spread over different ranges; in theory the isolines on one map, though omitted from the other, would occupy identical positions on both maps if they had to be drawn in.

As might be expected from the theory underlying their construction, isoline maps are best suited to illustrating distributions where changes are relatively gradual; they are particularly unsuited to distributions which are patchy or uneven, especially where the areas used as a basis are many and small. Circumstances such as this will often produce very contrived isoline patterns unless the isoline values are so widely spaced that a great many of the minor variations in the figures can be ignored. This explains the apparent ease with which layer-coloured isoline maps are often used in atlases to show such notoriously varied and irregularly distributed quantities as population density. Observation will show that each colour covers a very wide range of density, often increasing irregularly in a 'geometrical' way, e.g. by using 0, 8, 16, 64, 128, 256 and 512 persons per square mile as critical values; if *detail* has to be maintained in a patchy distribution a shading map will often allow easier construction and give better results.

REPEATED QUANTITATIVE SYMBOLS

Many of the methods used for showing the distribution of quantities at a series of points can be adapted for use with quantities relating to areas. As the methods have already been described it will only be necessary here to review those aspects which are particularly relevant to this new task.

The idea of representing quantity contained within an area by a single symbol has a strong appeal in many cases. As we have seen, techniques relating to areas frequently need quantities expressed in a particular way so that the map shall not be confused by the effect of the varying size of the units used; but the answer may prove to be rather unrepresentative. The whole concept of density of distribution within an area, for example, is often more theoretical than real; to say that within a given area the average density is 1,000 persons per square mile means nothing other than that the population in that unit is 1,000 times greater than the area, measured in square miles, and the figure may or may not have the remotest resemblance to conditions within the area. If this resemblance is known to be slight or doubtful it might be best to abandon such artificial concepts and stick to one symbol placed within the area and representing the actual quantity concerned.

Unfortunately the results are often much less successful than when similar ideas are applied to point values, for where figures relating to areas are used what matters is frequently not the actual quantity but the variations in distribution from area to area which it implies. It is, of course, precisely for this reason that concepts such as density are introduced at all and it must be admitted that the alternative of piecing together the same picture from a large number of varying symbols, each attached to an area also varying in size, is not very successful. Fig. 16c (p. 47), which illustrates land in farms in Michigan treated by this method, brings out the disadvantages which so often result. It is always difficult to strike a balance between a suitable symbol size range and the areas within which these must be contained, e.g. in Fig. 16c the rather large symbols make it impossible to add the rectangular boundary lines without causing confusion. The method is too 'rigid' and lacks any element which helps the eye to move from one part of the map to another. A more flexible quantitative symbol, such as the dot, will usually achieve a much better result. Another example, drawn in a slightly different context, will be found in Fig. 34 (p. 96).

REPEATED STATISTICAL DIAGRAMS

Statistical diagrams, of the kind described at the beginning of this chapter are also often encountered drawn on a map base to illustrate variations in several factors throughout an area. The method has some of the same potential and problems as repeated quantitative symbols, for once again the resultant effect is produced by several individual items scattered about the face of the map. Its success depends on the purpose which the map is intended to serve.

In some cases the map is little more than a visual geographical index to diagrams which would be drawn in any case, and where this is so it may be sensible, if room permits, to place these on a map background which will illustrate their location and allow minor comparisons, e.g. between neighbours, to be made as well. In many other examples, however, it would appear that far more than this is required of the method and the map user is being asked to piece together from these many scattered items a picture of the variations in distribution which they indicate throughout the map. This is surely asking too much. It is difficult enough to evaluate the relationship between symbol and area and its variation over the map when quantitative symbols are being used, it is almost impossible to do this when we have not a simple geometrical shape but a complex diagram such as a graph or pie graph, which may contain several variable elements all relevant to the theme of the map.

Fig. 18 illustrates, in a manner commonly employed for this purpose, the relative importance of different types of land use in the provinces of the Netherlands and the weaknesses of the method can be seen fairly easily, even on this relatively simple example. It is not difficult to obtain an impression of the importance of the different uses in any one province, nor even to compare this with its neighbours, but it *would* be to try to maintain this comparison over the whole of the map to obtain a composite picture of land use distribution throughout the kingdom; it is not even certain that the map would be a very reliable way of obtaining an impression of the varying distribution of only one element, e.g. arable land, let alone five.

KEY TO INSET

$\frac{2}{3}$ ARABLE

$\frac{1}{2}-\frac{2}{3}$ GRASS'D.

$\frac{1}{3}$ { ARABLE
GRASS'D.

OTHER NOTABLE USES
SHOWN BY LETTERS
[SEE BELOW]

KEY TO LAND USE

GRASSLAND   ARABLE

X WASTE   HORTICULTURE H

WOODLAND
W

MILES
0   20   40

Fig. 18. Land Utilisation in the Provinces of the Netherlands shown by repeated statistical diagrams (Pie Graphs). The inset map is added to summarise the situation portrayed on the main map and thus help interpretation. *Source:* Central Bureau Voor de Statistik, *Jaarcijfers Voor Nederland 1957-8*, Zeist, 1960.

61

Fig. 19. Distribution of Rainfall in Australia shown by: (*a*) *Fig. 19A.* Repeated Statistical Diagrams (Bar Graphs). (*b*) *Fig. 19B* (opposite). The same method with the message of the symbols emphasised by annotation recording main themes. Most maps using repeated statistical diagrams would benefit by annotation of some kind, bringing out essential points from amongst a welter of detail. *Source:* Meteorological Office, *Tables of Temperature, Relative Humidity and Precipitation for the World (Part VI),* London (H.M.S.O.), 1958.

The trouble here is that the cartographer has done too little work on his statistics and left the really hard job of correlation to the map user. The responsibility for evaluating the important aspects of any distribution should always rest with the cartographer who should first determine these and then illustrate them in map form, e.g. by adding an inset diagram, as has been done here. Reliance on visual comparison by the map user is no substitute for this direct mapping of relevant details. The same problem occurs where change in a situation is illustrated by mapping it at two different dates. If changes are *really* important then they should be mapped separately and not be left to a comparison of two maps.

In all fairness it should be added that it is very tempting to try to use this method of dealing with rather complex distributions, for the simple reason that it manages to kill so many birds with one stone. It is possible, for example, as in Fig. 19A to try to illustrate variations in rainfall throughout the year in Australia by drawing on a map of that continent a series of small bar graphs showing mean monthly rainfall at selected stations. Without any further help this provides an impossible amount of detail for the map user to assess; an

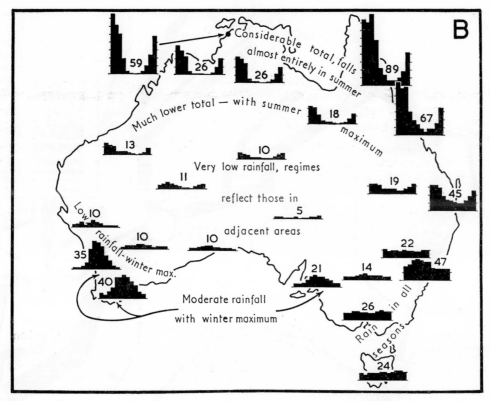

Fig. 19B.

alternative might be found by constructing not one map but a series of isoline maps showing, say, mean monthly rainfall only for January, April, July and October, although this still leaves a considerable amount of comparison to be done if a composite picture for the whole year is required. Another possibility lies in amplifying the original method by examining the detailed statistics further, ruthlessly eliminating detail and determining any major similarities in yearly régime which exist at any of the stations shown. If these characteristic similarities are then marked on the map as a general guide, the usefulness of the individual diagrams is much increased. General trends are already selected and the diagrams can supplement these by indicating any minor variations within the major themes. Fig. 19B shows how much more useful such an annotated map is than the 'bald' diagrammatic representation in Fig. 19A. Other types of statistics with several variables, e.g. for land use or industrial structure, could be treated in a similar way, e.g. Fig. 47 where background shading replaces annotation.

QUANTITIES DISTRIBUTED ALONG A LINE

Of all the major groups of quantitative statistical maps this is by far the simplest to describe, for only one method is in common use. The quantities portrayed are almost always traffic flows along routeways of various kinds and the method used is to draw, astride each route, a band proportional in width to the quantity of traffic passing.

Fig. 20. Local Passenger Trains on Railways in Part of South Wales, 1955, shown by bands of proportional width. *Source: Bradshaw's British Railways Guide, July, 1955*, London, 1955.

The idea is quite successful, but it should be noticed that the scale of band-widths is a linear one and, as with all such scales, an extended range of values cannot easily be accommodated. Where such a range has to be dealt with a convenient modification is to adopt a series of graduated band-widths, designed after the manner of the graduated range of symbols for point values which were described earlier. Fig. 20 shows an example of such a map.

The methods described in this chapter have been taken in the order set out in Fig. 2 (p. 16). As that diagram itself suggests some methods can be used in the presentation of more than one kind of distributional pattern and it will have become apparent from the text that even more cross-linkages are possible. The particular choice of one method out of the several which are available to tackle some problems will depend on many factors, and particularly on certain general considerations which will be described in Chapter 4, but before any such choice is made it is often desirable to have a look at the statistics themselves. These will form the raw material for whichever method is chosen and some of the more important aspects of their character are considered in the next chapter.

CHAPTER THREE

Sense from Statistics: The Search for the Significant

I T is remarkably easy to slip into the habit of summarising a situation statistically. We tend to say, for example, that in Bloggsbridge Urban District 55% of the women under thirty are brunettes, 40% are blondes and 5% are red-heads, in preference to saying (what amounts to the same thing) that there are rather more brunettes than blondes whilst red-heads are quite uncommon. One great advantage in using the statistical approach in preference to the descriptive one is that it *seems* to be so much more precise and it makes comparisons with other places so much simpler. Similar figures for the neighbouring Urban District of Mudworth, for example, would immediately make it apparent to those gentlemen who prefer blondes whether their efforts are more likely to come to a successful conclusion if transferred to that locality.[1]

This idea of using a series of statistics as a sort of shorthand summary of a complex situation at one place and from them making comparisons with other places is so common a procedure that it is easy to use it in rather a slipshod manner. If the method is to succeed at all one absolute prerequisite is that the statistics used to represent conditions at a place should *really* do so, and should have their roots in geographical reality and not, as so often happens, in administrative convenience or mathematical calculations, both of which are capable of producing answers which are not only inaccurate but quite unlike any set of conditions which actually exist.

We have already encountered the problem of unrepresentative values when considering techniques for presenting quantities relating to a given area and it is worth while looking rather more deeply into this general problem. Of the two main causes of unrepresentative figures mentioned above, those which derive from administrative causes are probably the most difficult to detect and the most difficult to overcome. A major source of this difficulty lies in the fact that many people who need statistical information to help them with a particular problem have to use statistics which are provided by other agencies, often for quite different purposes. Occasionally it may be possible to devise and obtain privately exactly those

---

[1] This is not strictly true, of course. All that comparative statistics of the above type would indicate is the probability of *encountering* ladies of a particular hair colouring. What happens after that would depend on many things, amongst which statistics of quite a different type might play a part.

statistics which are needed to carry out a task but even here, to save time or expense, there is a tendency to incorporate or at least start out from, statistics obtained from other sources such as a national census. Censuses and similar publications by government departments or large-scale organisations such as UNO are invaluable to the statistical cartographer simply because they offer information in considerable detail on a wide range of subjects; unfortunately, they almost inevitably involve certain disadvantages which are characteristic of 'other people's statistics' and a sensible awareness of these disadvantages can do much to improve the quality of any work which derives from this type of source material.

The fundamental principle which should be kept in mind when using official statistics of any sort is that these are a means to an end rather than an end in itself. Official statistics are not an implacable umpire whose pronouncements must be complied with lest they be 'used in evidence against you', but are instead a valuable source of information which may need certain modifications before it can be used for the work in hand.

The most unsatisfactory feature which pertains to 'other people's statistics' is usually the units or areas for which individual figures are given. These are almost always the various types of administrative subdivision of a country or large organisation (such as British Railways or the National Coal Board), and though these may be well devised as a basis for administering that country or organisation they may be much less meaningful in terms of other aspects of everyday life, and statistics which relate to them may be less useful generally than one might expect. It is surprising, but apparently true, that when official statistics are being prepared, little consideration is given to their potential use outside the narrow administrative framework or to the possibility of modifying their published form to suit the general user. Let us take a simple example.

The population of a city is often quoted to give some indication of its size and the kind of place it is. Any foreign person who consults a standard reference work on Britain will find that the populations (in thousands) of the largest English cities outside London were, in 1961

Birmingham	1,106	Sheffield	494
Liverpool	747	Bristol	436
Manchester	661	Nottingham	312
Leeds	511		

A moment's thought and a glance at a 1-in. Ordnance Survey map will soon make it apparent that as a guide to size and 'kind of place' these figures have not a great deal of meaning. Many British people would be able to help a less well-informed foreigner by pointing out that Salford, with 156,000 population was simply part of the Mancunian rose smelling as sweetly by another name, but would they also realise that something so essentially 'Manchester' as the Trafford Park Industrial Estate is not technically so but is situated in Stretford Municipal Borough next door? In the list above only the figures given for Sheffield, Leeds and, perhaps, Bristol begin to approach being representative of what most people think of as these towns. Nottingham, and Newcastle to take another example, are both surrounded by suburban 'Urban' Districts, and the inclusion with Newcastle of no more than Gateshead alters the picture completely and brings that city up from 12th to 7th place in the list. A revised list incorporating only the most obvious additions presents quite a different picture:

Birmingham-Smethwick	1,173	Bristol	436
Manchester-Salford-Stretford	877	Nottingham-Arnold-Carlton-	
Liverpool-Bootle	830	West Bridgeford	404
Leeds	511	Newcastle-Gateshead	373
Sheffield	494		

Equally misleading are the mythical entities which occur from time to time in official figures. The gathering together of six towns,[1] none of which is more than medium sized, may produce the City of Stoke-on-Trent with 266,000 people, but this is not remotely to be compared with a place such as Leicester (273,000), nor is the agglomeration of mining villages which make up the Rhondda Municipal Borough (100,000) anything like, say, Northampton (105,000); yet these bare official figures are widely quoted whenever information is rapidly sought and comparisons are not infrequently based on them. Whilst it is relatively easy to make allowances for discrepancies of this kind in the more familiar circumstances of one's own country it is far easier to overlook them when using foreign statistics; an ambitious attempt to help overcome this difficulty on a world scale has been published recently under the title of *The World's Metropolitan Areas*,[2] in which populations are given for urban *agglomerations* (rather than individual administrative units) all over the world, provided the total population is more than 100,000. In some instances the criteria adopted produce results that are more apparent than real; many British readers will be surprised to learn of the existence of an Aldershot-Farnborough 'Metropolitan' area and however contiguous they may appear on the ground Leeds and Bradford can in no respect be considered a single functional entity, despite persistent attempts, here and elsewhere, to treat them as such. Minor quibbles about what may be essentially subjective judgements are not the main point here, however. The figures produced represent the approach of one team of workers to this particularly important problem and the attempt is to be commended for making some contribution towards its solution on a world scale.

In a very few cases more representative figures are published in official sources to help overcome these anomalies. Thus the *Statistisches Jahrbuch der Schweiz 1959/60*, quoting figures for the populations of Switzerland's principal urban centres, gives the two types of value listed below, the first a purely 'administrative' one and the second a more 'real' or 'functional' one; the differences are quite marked, usually of the order of 20-40%.

It is not surprising therefore, that the plotting of 'crude' official figures will often produce maps which are much less representative than they should be, and a sensible rule to adopt is never to plot on a map any information which is *known* to be misleading or meaningless. Quite often it is possible, with only a little research or calculation, to produce figures which, though they may result from subjective judgement and be open to criciticsm on the grounds of inaccuracy, are much more real and representative than the original ones.

[1] *Pace* Arnold Bennett, there really are six.
[2] International Urban Research, *The World's Metropolitan Areas*, University of California Press, 1954.

SWITZERLAND—POPULATION OF MAIN CENTRES, 1958

Centre	Population of Commune at Centre (i.e. main town)	Population of 'Agglomeration'
Zürich	437	528
Basel	205	292
Genève	174	228
Bern	165	223
Lausanne	123	157
Luzern	67	117

Unfortunately, one encounters all too often maps where convenience of source material seems to have been the only selective criterion used in compiling the map. An example of these defects and their possible improvement is shown in Fig. 21 which illustrates the distribution of urban population in the central West Riding of Yorkshire in 1951.

Fig. 21. Population of Urban Areas in Part of the West Riding of Yorkshire, 1951. In Fig. 21A Urban Areas are defined on a purely administrative basis; Fig. 21B refers to the actual physical units 'on the ground'.
Source: (Fig. 21A) Registrar-General, *Census of England and Wales, 1951*, County Volume: Yorkshire (West Riding), London (H.M.S.O.), 1954.

Fig. 21A shows this in a manner similar to that used in the 'Population of Urban Areas' map published by the Ordnance Survey and deals only in the population of the administrative units in the area; Fig. 21B ignores local government boundaries and attempts to show the actual population of the physical units which form the urban structure of the area. Within the West Riding the boundary revisions of the 1930's often grouped together former small Urban Districts based on the large industrial 'villages' (of about 5,000 to 7,000 population) and the few *small* towns which lie in the area between the large county boroughs; the resulting medium-sized 'towns' which appear on Fig. 21A are unreal entities and, as Fig. 21B shows, there are almost no medium-sized units of between 25,000 and 45,000 population within the area of the map. It is ironical to note that though populations in this area are generally fairly static and have been so for some time Fig. 21A would have had a completely different appearance if it had been prepared before the boundary changes occurred. To be quite fair, the Ordnance Survey's map does not purport to show the population of towns in Britain but only of 'urban areas', but the latter term is an equivocal one and if the appellation 'urban' is applied to administrative units in as meaningless a way as is the case in Great Britain the picture which the map portrays will be of limited usefulness.

Not only do meaningless quantitative statistics give a false picture of a particular place, they render comparisons with other places of doubtful reliability. Suppose for example that we wish to compare regional structure around Leeds and Newcastle-upon-Tyne by studying the part which commuting plays in providing part of the labour force of each town. In 1951 the commuting figures for the two towns were as follows:

	Leeds	Newcastle	Newcastle and Gateshead
Number of jobs	265,000	175,000	219,000
Number of commuters	34,000	65,000	62,000
Commuters as percentage of total jobs	13	37	28

It has already been pointed out that the City of Leeds is a relatively meaningful entity whereas the City of Newcastle is not and if Gateshead is added to Newcastle and movement from one to the other ignored we get the adjusted figures given in the third column. True, the difference between 'Newcastle' and Leeds is still quite considerable, but in view of the ring of suburban 'urban' districts which lie around Newcastle and the fact that even in Leeds one of the main concentrations of industry occupying possibly 2,500 workers lies just outside the city boundary, one is left wondering whether the difference is really so large as it appears to be and whether it does not originate largely in the peculiar administrative framework of the Newcastle area.

The administrative complications which beset official statistics are well known if not well heeded. Another much less obvious cause of poor representational quality can derive from what might be termed 'mathematical complications'. A major common defect of statistics is that taken down to their smallest unit they are too prolific, either for assimilation or even for general publication, so that they have to be summarised or given as average values for increasingly large units, these larger units being frequently administrative subdivisions such as Rural Districts, counties, provinces or regions. Many people who make use of such averages or summary figures rarely pause to consider the limitations of these strictly mathematical devices which attempt to replace a series or group of values by one significant value. The usefulness of the average, for example, depends entirely on the range and composition of the group of values from which it was derived, and it may be either highly significant or almost meaningless according to circumstances.

The statistics which form the basis of Fig. 22 provide some interesting examples of the way in which these factors can work. They relate to population change in the North Riding of Yorkshire between 1931 and 1951 and were taken from the Census of the latter date. It would be possible of course to obtain one figure to represent the change within the whole county (it is in fact +12·6%) but with a unit which embraces extensive moorland areas and industrial Tees-side further subdivision is obviously necessary. If the county is divided into 'rural' areas (i.e. Rural Districts) and 'urban' areas (i.e. the remainder) the figures for these sections would be $+20\cdot9\%$ and $+11\cdot0\%$ respectively. Now an increase of $+20\cdot9\%$ would be startling enough in any rural area let alone one which is often barren and remote, and this figure invites further subdivision into its constituent Rural Districts. The figures for each of these show $+20\cdot9\%$ to be quite useless as a representative value, for of the 20 constituent Districts, 11 showed an increase but 9 showed a decrease; and if we take out only the two most extreme cases (Richmond and Flaxton R.D.'s) the figure for the remainder is at once reduced to $+9\cdot1\%$. Even this figure is an uneasy representative of the very varied conditions encountered, and the obvious course would be to treat each Rural District separately.

Maps such as Fig. 22A which do just that are quite common in British literature and it is worth while looking to see whether we have achieved any more reasonable a solution. Sometimes we have. Aysgarth R.D. had a total change of $-15\cdot3\%$ and of its 12 parishes all but one showed a decrease and of these 8 were within 3% of the figure for the whole Rural District; here is a case where the district figure is real and meaningful. Contrast this with Northallerton R.D. where of 41 parishes 20 showed increase, 21 decrease, only 23 came within 5% of the average figure and the range ran from $+76\cdot5\%$ to -75%. In Wath R.D. an aerodrome constructed in one parish completely falsifies the picture for the whole Rural District $(+49\cdot8\%)$; without this exceptional case the other 10 parishes give a total change of $-7\cdot6\%$. The average value, or a summary figure, is often of doubtful utility because it may cover up very varying conditions and particularly because it is too much affected by extreme values, allowing them to play an important part in determining the final figure.

To remove these unrepresentative values for the large units the next step would appear to be to descend to even smaller areas, in this case the constituent parishes. We could, of course, calculate the change in each parish in a Rural District and calculate the average of these, but like all averages this would be affected by extreme values.[1] Alternatively, we could use the *median*, another mathematical device which produces a representative value for a group of figures but which is less affected by extremes. The median value of any group of figures is quite easily determined; it is simply the middle value when they are arranged in ascending order. If any value occurs more than once all its occurrences are included, and if there is an even number of items so that there cannot be a middle value the convention is to give as median the quantity which lies half-way between the two values which lie astride the middle.

The great asset of the median is that exceptional and freak values in a run of figures get no more weight in the final figure than any other constituent, so that if the great majority of the constituents have normal values but there are two or three freak values in the range, the median is likely to be far more representative than the average. On the other hand if the constituents themselves have a wide range generally, as in the case of Northallerton R.D. referred to above, neither the median nor the average will be very representative, and further subdivision into more homogeneous units is the only way to achieve better results.

Figs. 22B and C show something of this rationalising process in action and indicate how

---

[1] For Wath R.D. referred to above the figure produced in this way is $+39\cdot8\%$, entirely due to the fact that the parish with the aerodrome increased by 530%, which is quite enough to overwhelm any average.

Fig. 22. Population Change in the North Riding of Yorkshire, 1931-51, showing the different results obtained when different types of area and unit are used as the basis of the change, namely: *Fig. 22A.* Average change for whole Rural and Urban Districts. *Fig. 22B.* Median of change in individual parishes in each Rural and Urban District. *Fig. 22C.* Average change for 'rationalised' units, see text. *Source:* Registrar-General, *Census of England and Wales, 1951*, County Volume, Yorkshire (East and North Ridings), London (H.M.S.O.), 1954.

important sensible treatment of a series of figures can be if a good result is to be obtained. Fig. 22A has already been examined and shows the change when measured by the easiest available published figure—namely, that for whole administrative units. Fig. 22B replaces these misleading values by the *median* value of the changes in *individual parishes* in each Rural District. The difference is startling and a good example of how the effect of a few extreme values was spread over a wide area in Fig. 22A. Unfortunately, Fig. 22B achieves this improvement at the expense of almost concealing the fact that there was any marked increase in rural areas; and Fig. 22C attempts to rectify this by giving figures for the total change in smaller, more homogeneous units which could easily be produced by removing obvious anomalies within each Rural District. Thus all small towns which were not officially 'urban' in status but which were quite distinct from the mass of settlements in the rural area were treated separately or in conjunction with any 'overflow' into neighbouring parishes. Also treated separately were any other parishes with more than 800 people, or any with a 'remarkable' change, i.e. more than $+50\%$ or $-33\cdot3\%$ provided the population exceeded 100 in 1931. Small detached portions of any area were not allowed but were added to the most similar adjoining large unit, and some of the peculiar Urban Districts in the north were subdivided into an urban core and rural fringe. Fig. 22C naturally involved more work than Figs. 22A and B, but the result was worth while. The general pattern of rural decrease stands out quite well with the 'plums in the pudding' distribution of the exceptional values seen in their true perspective. However, figures are still given for inconveniently large areas; the devices used were chosen because they were easily applied (hence the choice of $+50\%$ and $-33\cdot3\%$) and further possibilities for dealing with these figures will be examined in Chapter 6.

Many of the defects just described arose from trying to obtain figures for areas which were too big to have any meaning. Oddly enough it is possible to obtain somewhat parallel defects because the areas used are too small, so that statistics relating to them are too easily affected by random occurrences. Many of the rural parishes within the North Riding have ridiculously small populations; there are 592 of them in all and of these 297 have populations of less than 200 and the most common size groups are 50-59 population (24 parishes) and 70-79 population (25 parishes). In units as small as this, chance happenings can quite markedly affect the picture. Farmer Giles's wife producing her sixth child a couple of days before census night automatically boosts the population by 1 to 2%; the demise of the oldest inhabitant at ninety-four a month later quite fails to redeem the official statistical situation. In larger units such as urban areas happenings of this kind[1] are sufficiently frequent to cancel one another out and allow long-term trends to show through, but in small rural parishes they can quite easily cause arbitrary and misleading figures. It is often difficult to decide with small units just how large a change need be before it can be regarded as significant and not 'accidental'.

There is no easy way round the administrative and mathematical difficulties which other people's statistics so often present. The only safeguard is to know one's area, one's statistics and their limitations and to concentrate more on the figures one wants rather than be obsessed by the statistics one has got. The examples above come mostly from British figures relating to population, but there are equal pitfalls in other branches. Figures for commuting,

[1] Births and deaths generally, not necessarily of sixth children or nonagenarians.

for example, are seriously affected by the size of the unit used, so long as crossing a boundary line remains an essential definition; in the Industry Tables of the last British Census employment in garages, which most people would rate as a typical service or tertiary industry, and which frequently employs 3% or more of the labour force of a town, is returned with Order VII, Vehicles, a predominantly manufacturing or secondary industrial group. If primary, secondary and tertiary industrial ratios are being determined, here is a group which ought properly to be transferred before totals are abstracted.

In this chapter so far, the main concern has been to find a significant value which could be used to represent a given statistical situation on a map. In another sense too, every good statistical map should illustrate this 'search for the significant' by ensuring that it emphasises the really important facts in a situation. Detail should not be allowed to dominate the map and obscure the main messages it has to show. Unfortunately, one encounters all too often maps which appear to be suffering from 'statistical indigestion', maps filled with detail amongst which the poor map user has to ferret around to sort out what matters and what does not. What are we *really* expected to deduce from the map which contains 44 pie graphs all divided into six sectors, or 72 circles all of varying sizes?—certainly we shall be lucky if we obtain an impression at all commensurate with the tremendous amount of work which went into the production of the map. This point of statistical indigestion has already been touched upon when considering repeated statistical diagrams as a possible technique. The solution suggested there was for the cartographer to reduce and remove some of the many variables by attempting a classification of the raw material; simpler techniques may not need such drastic treatment—the replacement of a range of proportional circles simply by one of graduated symbols will help the map user to handle and appreciate large numbers of quantities at once, and so will the addition of a small 'Summary diagram' as has been done in Fig. 18 (p. 61).

More will be said of increasing the actual legibility of the various techniques in the next chapter, but in the present context the moral is obvious. It is not good enough to say, in effect, 'I am working on a pretty complex statistical situation and here is a pretty complex statistical map to prove it!' Presumably, the person who devised such a complicated map has studied this situation, understands it and should be able to sort things out and offer to the map user a really stimulating visual aid which will help him to grasp the situation, instead of getting practically the whole of the statistical material put in front of him, pictorially translated but virtually unsorted. Almost the only reason for presenting masses of statistics seems to be the idea of showing the reader the whole of the raw material from which the study began but when illustrations are limited in number, as they often are, this is rather a wasted opportunity. Unfortunately such maps cannot usually be used to advantage as a 'statistical quarry', either, for they frequently present the information in a way which makes it impossible to read it back quickly from the map.

There is a distinct limit to the amount which can be incorporated onto a map and appreciated by looking at it. It is by no means a bad plan not merely to ask oneself, 'What do I want this map to show?' but to have a list of priorities in this respect and be prepared to sacrifice some of the less important aims if they tend to obscure the picture.

The considerations which have been stressed in this chapter refer particularly to formal statistical maps—the finished material which accompanies presentation of a piece of work; in the early stages of research it often happens that statistical maps are being used as a *source* of ideas, rather than as happens later to *represent* ideas. At this early stage rough maps, quickly drawn from crude statistics will, and often must, suffice. It is only as work on the topic progresses that the refinements described above can be added, or the freak values and unrepresentative average adjusted as a result of further information. The main ideas of the study will also emerge and it is at this later stage that the design of the final maps should be considered. Experience with rough maps will often help too in the choice of a suitable technique for the final presentation, but other considerations which surround this important decision are discussed in the next chapter.

Limitation of the number of illustrations which can be provided to accompany any piece of work, whether by reason of space, cost or both, may make it necessary to consider another major point concerning the statistics themselves. If it is possible to have only one map or diagram to illustrate each main distribution it becomes important to decide which *aspect* of the figures shall be presented. Even the simplest set of figures can usually be looked at from more than one point of view and where space is limited it is essential to consider which is the most relevant aspect of the problem in hand. It is not sufficient to imagine 'I will have a map to show population distribution, or agricultural production, or commuting in an area', for example, for each of these is capable of being presented in different ways, bringing out different points and having rather dissimilar adaptations.

Consider Fig. 23 which illustrates this idea for the last of the three examples given above and shows aspects of the journey to work in Central London from the Home Counties area. Fig. 23A is a simple quantitative map prepared by a variation of the dot method. It shows the number of daily commuters to Central London but deals with this figure in isolation and in no way attempts to relate these numbers to any other aspect of life within the region; its main uses would be twofold for it offers answers to the questions, 'Where does Central London's labour come from?' and, less definitely, 'How many people travel daily from X to Central London?' Transport authorities would find the information presented in this way particularly useful in illustrating the amount and extent of the daily movements with which they must cope.

Fig. 23B presents the same basic information in quite a different way for it deals not directly with numbers but with relative numbers or percentages. The commuters to Central London are now expressed as a percentage of the total labour force in each area but no indication is given of the actual number of people involved. Instead emphasis is placed on the relative importance in each area of employment in Central London, with all its implications for the student of regional association or structure and the degree of 'dormitoriness' of any particular place. To anyone involved in an attempt to plan the region as a whole considerations of this sort might be more important at first than sheer numbers.

Fig. 23C is similar in principle to Fig. 23B, but modifies its approach slightly. Because of the predominance of employment in service industries in Britain even the most suburban areas contain quite a large number of jobs so that the percentages in Fig. 23B never rise quite so high as the stream of city-bound workers each morning might suggest. In 1951 areas such as Orpington Urban District with 27,199 workers within its boundaries still had 16,221 jobs

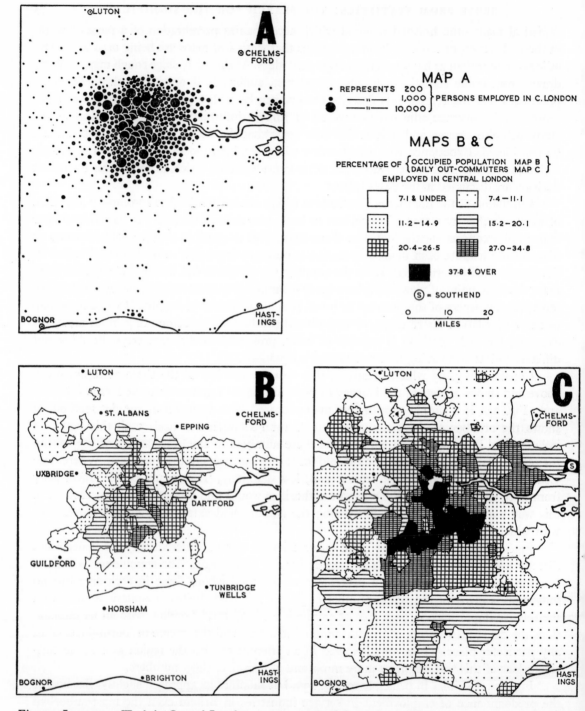

Fig. 23. Journey to Work in Central London, 1951, examined from three different points of view. In these maps 'Central London' means the cities of London and Westminster and the Metropolitan Borough of Holborn. *Source:* Registrar-General, *Census of England and Wales, 1951.* Usual Residence and Workplace Volume, London (H.M.S.O.), 1956.

to offer them, and the 5,916 city commuters, despite their sizeable total, form only 22% of the labour force. Fig. 23C attempts to counteract this considerable block of 'irreducible' home-based employment by dealing only in commuters, expressing the Central London workers as a percentage of all outgoing travellers. Attention here is focused not on the part commuting plays in the local way of life, nor on the contribution each area makes to Central London but on the commuter himself. It answers the question, 'What proportion of the inhabitants of X who get up and leave their home area to go to work each day are "city-gents" and what proportion are bound elsewhere?'

The division between the aspects of the figures involved in Fig. 23A and Figs. 23B and C is a fundamental and obvious one; that between Figs. 23B and C themselves is rather more subtle, but with marked differences emerging. One of the most remarkable totals on Fig. 23A is that of daily commuters from Southend to London, 7,452 in all. Fig. 23B shows, however, that in the light of the employment offered by a town the size of Southend this movement does not form a large percentage (11·8%) of the total labour force, but in Fig. 23C we can observe that if people *do* leave Southend to go to work elsewhere they tend particularly to go to Central London for this purpose, this movement amounting to 38·9% of all commuters and being quite remarkable in size for a town so far from Central London.

It is the ability to present different aspects of figures in this way which leads to the popular belief that 'you can prove anything with statistics' or that 'you can make statistics say anything you like'. Let us try to do just that. We will suppose that the Bloggsbridge Urban District Council have designs to incorporate within their area the Urban District of Mudworth and that one of the benefits they claim that they can offer is that Bloggsbridge provides a higher standard of urban amenities than its smaller neighbour; being thoroughly 'publicity-minded' they decide to initiate a poster campaign to influence public opinion in Mudworth and are currently devoting their attention to shopping facilities. The position is this:

BLOGGSBRIDGE AND MUDWORTH—SHOPPING FACILITIES

	Bloggsbridge U.D.	Mudworth U.D.
Population	24,000	12,000
Number of Shops, 1961	400	100
Persons per Shop, 1961	60	120
Number of Shops, 1945	360	63
Percentage increase in Shops, 1945-61	11	60

The figures seem overwhelmingly to help Bloggsbridge, who therefore campaign in the manner of Fig. 24A. The men of Mudworth know a thing or two, however. In terms of quantity, even of quality, their case is hopeless. The gloomy Victorian façades of the Mudworth Co-operative Society and 'Manchester House' or the bizarre advertisements outside 'Joe's Murder Shop'[1] are poor assets to set against Bloggsbridge's Woolworth's, Marks and Spencer's or the emporium of Joshua Bloggs Ltd.;[2] they must find some other aspect of the

[1] 'We don't slash prices—we *murder* 'em!'   [2] 'Buy it at Bloggs'!' (registered trade mark).

figures if they are to succeed in counteracting the impression put forward by their neighbours. Their answer lies, as Fig. 24B shows, in quite another approach—namely, a consideration of what has been done recently. Mudworth, like many another small industrial town, has prospered unusually since the war and the new shops added in this phase provide just the ammunition which is needed.

Fig. 24. Two Contending Parties each Deriving Advantage from the same statistical situation by concentrating on different aspects of the figures. Notice that once one has decided to be thoroughly biased it is easy to introduce further visual overtones—the suggestion of a perpetual queue at Mudworth shops in Fig. 24A or that only shops built post-1945 are modern in Fig. 24B are examples of this.

Their case is in many ways already lost and is based on a statistical quibble but it illustrates the remarkable effect which choice of aspect can have in depicting a situation and the danger of accepting statistical values without as full a knowledge as possible of their background. All too often figures illustrating only one narrow aspect of a complicated situation are presented with great confidence and assurance as providing the last incontrovertible word on any particular point. It is essential, so long as statistics continue to be presented to the public in support of policies and points of view, that their limitations as well as their advantages should be recognised.

CHAPTER FOUR

Choosing the Right Method and Making the Most of It

A REVIEW of the techniques which are available and the statistical pitfalls which may be encountered has placed us in a position to decide how to choose a technique for a particular task and begin the actual plotting of the information. The couple of dozen or so methods which were described in Chapter 2 will have made it apparent that in dealing with most statistical distributions there *is* a choice of method available and this chapter describes some of the broad considerations which may influence the final decision.

One important point which emerges from Chapter 2 and Fig. 2 (p. 16) together is that the amount of choice will depend greatly on the type of statistical base which is being used, figures for point values, or values along a line offering less possible variety than figures relating to areas where a wide choice is possible. A useful rule to adopt in these cases is that the best method is the one which *looks* right and which conveys an impression which most closely resembles the kind of distribution which the cartographer envisages in his own mind.

Figs. 25A, B, C and D show different ways of illustrating the distribution of population in South-west Lancashire. The figures used were the 1951 populations of civil parishes and in Fig. 25A this total has been represented by proportional symbols, one symbol for each parish. In Fig. 25B a dot map with one dot for every 250 persons is used whilst Fig. 25C combines these methods, using dots for rural areas but proportional symbols for all units over 10,000 population which appeared to have definite urban quality. Fig. 25D turns to another aspect of the figures and illustrates the distribution by means of a density shading map. If the main aim of such a map was simply to present a general picture of population distribution in South-west Lancashire, describing where people were and in what manner they were distributed on the ground, the author's preference would undoubtedly go to Fig. 25C which most nearly corresponds to his impression of the way in which the population is actually distributed—a rural scatter of population varying in density with some areas quite thickly peopled (as in the coalfield for example) interspersed with important urban centres of varying size. Fig. 25A is too rigid to be satisfactory, for the division between symbol and background is too clear cut to reflect reality; Fig. 25B is much better and conveys a good deal of the impression needed, especially where the dots coalesce at the larger centres. Where Fig. 25C scores over Fig. 25B is that by introducing a new type of symbol it is able to distinguish

Fig. 25. Distribution of Population in South-west Lancashire, 1951, shown by: (*a*) *Fig. 25A.* Proportional circles for the population of each civil parish. (*b*) *Fig. 25B.* Dots, one dot for every 250 persons. (*c*) *Fig. 25C.* Proportional circles for the population of each urban centre over 10,000 population with dots for the remaining areas. (*d*) *Fig. 25D.* By shading according to the population density in each civil parish. The whole figure offers a useful opportunity to see the different impressions produced when the same information is treated by four different methods. This diagram is freely adapted from an idea in F. J. Monkhouse and H. R. Wilkinson, *Maps and Diagrams*, p. 236, London, 1952. *Source:* Registrar-General, *Census of England and Wales, 1951*, County Volume, Lancashire; London (H.M.S.O.), 1954.

sharply between population concentrated in the main urban centres and that in other areas whilst at the same time it offers a chance of giving positive information about the size of those centres, which Fig. 25B cannot. Fig. 25D, by dealing in density, introduces a rather imaginary measure-of-convenience for assessing this situation. If we were interested in density *for its own sake* there would be little to complain about in Fig. 25D, but if we are using it merely as an indirect way of summarising a distribution then its use seems far less satisfactory and it gives a much more incomplete picture than either Fig. 25B or C.

The use of a 'joint' method for dealing with a situation which has two basic components —urban and non-urban population—seems a sensible way of fitting a technique to the actual figures. It is not without its difficulties of course; the larger circular symbols sometimes overlap their area boundaries and make difficult the dispersal of dots within their neighbours, and where this occurs the dots are either omitted or, better, used to dot in the unfortunate 'blanks' which would have occurred at those points where the same circular symbol did not in fact reach the boundary line of the area which it represents. The small statistical 'fiddling' which this involves is not likely to upset the basic picture on the map, and it would have been foolish to abandon the whole method, with its useful overall impression, for the sake of one small point of difficulty.

Statistics relating to values within a given area offer the widest choice of possible techniques for their illustration and, as might be expected, it is with figures of this kind that there is the greatest danger of choosing a method which will look wrong. We have already seen that when shading and isoline maps are being used figures must be expressed in a way which will not be unduly influenced by variations in area, but even with quantitative techniques, such as dots evenly distributed throughout the area, it is easy to allow the effect of area to come through too sharply. No difficulty arises if the quantity being mapped is, in fact, tied to land area, for example acreage under a certain land use or even simple population distribution; but if its basic distribution is remote from consideration of area then a wrong effect may ensue.

Fig. 26 shows an illustration of this point. Fig. 26A represents the distribution of home areas of a student population by a dot technique. Information on this distribution was only available easily in terms of geographical counties and since further breakdown of the figures would have needed much more lengthy research the dots have been distributed evenly throughout each county with the added convenience of a summary total in the middle of each county area, any dots which would have been covered by this circle being omitted. The effect is not noticeably bad in the most extreme cases such as Lancashire and the West Riding where very high numbers still produce a dominant impression, but difficulties begin with the middle range of numbers where a visual effect is obtained which is by no means satisfactorily related to quantity. Contrast for example the effect produced in County Durham, the North and East Ridings by figures not particularly dissimilar in size. Here the density of dots and hence the visual impression is markedly affected by the *size* of the county concerned so that the larger North Riding comes out with a relatively much weaker impression. This is not at all the effect that is needed, for there is little or no relationship between what might be termed 'student-supply-potential' and superficial area and it is not desirable, therefore, to have this aspect of area influencing the map. Student-supply-potential, if it is related to anything at

FSM

Fig. 26. University of Leeds—Home Areas of Undergraduate Students, 1958–9. Of the two methods used the first is the least satisfactory, since it allows the impression of quantity to be affected by the area of the county, a factor which is quite irrelevant to the theme of the map; the second method avoids this pitfall. *Source:* Information supplied privately by the University Authorities.

all, will be more closely connected with population than anything else and since population in Britain has no definite relationship to superficial area the method has failed. To replace it there is needed a device which is not in the least affected by variation in area, and this is one situation where the single proportional symbol, as used in Fig. 26B, can successfully deal with statistics relating to areas.

In the example just described the dot symbol which *seems* so suited to representing a scattered group of people turns out to have unsuspected limitations and indeed, as Chapter 2 indicated, most methods in the group relating to areas have their own idiosyncrasies of effect. Dot maps are weak in quantitative impression, despite a quantitative base, excellent for showing general distribution, but poorly adapted to illustrating *small* differences should these be important. All too often one sees dot maps which, despite the greatest care and meticulous preparation, can be said to give no more than a general impression of fairly even distribution over the mass of the map with only a few exceptional areas standing out by coalescence of the dots—a great deal of work for a very general result. Shading maps, on the other hand, are excellent for emphasising differences (even quite small ones if necessary), give a clear, positive statement of quantity but may give a poor and rather artificial picture of distribution (e.g. Fig. 25D); isoline maps are best suited for illustrating distributions which show regular trends but in other ways they have some of the defects of shading maps. Density of colour is yet another factor of the areal techniques which needs matching to the actual figures and consideration of this aspect has already been made in Chapter 2.

A single example will serve to summarise many of these points. Suppose we have within an area a relatively even distribution which nevertheless shows small but important variations. A dot map would be of little use in representing such a distribution; a shading map with carefully planned shading limits would be better or, if the variations appeared to have a rational trend, even an isoline technique could be used. In either of the last two methods, however, range of colour would have to be kept fairly small so that once the method had picked out the differences they were not further emphasised out of proportion to their actual size.

Once the important choice of a particular method has been made it is obviously important to use it to its best advantage. Even the most well-selected techniques will not be put into practice without certain difficulties being encountered and the successful surmounting of these can add considerably to the finished effect of the map.

One of the most recurrent of these difficulties arises from the wide range of values which so often have to be accommodated. Chapter 2 showed that increased range may sometimes be dealt with by technical means, e.g. the use of areal or even volume symbols, but even so these devices frequently leave problems so far as the most extreme values are concerned. In many cases no completely satisfactory solution will be possible and the cartographer should guard against the danger of spoiling the design over 90% of the map simply by attempting to accommodate a few extreme values. In particular this applies to finding suitable sizes for proportional symbols which represent very small values in an extended range. Successful treatment of these lower values may well result in the bulk of the symbols being over-large and unwieldy and rather than do this it is worth while deciding whether these values are important enough to bother showing at all or, if so, whether all occurrences below a certain value cannot be shown by a uniform and very small symbol.

Extreme values at the upper end of the scale are not so easily tackled for, unlike the smaller ones, they are of extreme importance and cannot be ignored. One possible approach is to regard these values as extreme enough to amount to something quite different from the items forming the bulk of the map and if this is the case an easy choice is to 'break' the method being used and adopt an entirely different way of representing them. A very commonly recurring example of this is encountered in mapping rural populations by the dot technique. A dot value which is adjusted to small villages of 200 or even less population will not easily show a market town of, say, 20,000 population and even less an important local centre with 100,000. The village and the sizeable town are too unequal and dissimilar to fit into the same technique easily and, as Fig. 25c showed, a combination of two methods each capable of treating one of the two components will be much more successful.

The rule never to spoil the whole map for the sake of a few extremes can be applied in other contexts. The areas into which symbols have to be fitted are rarely of a suitably convenient shape and there will almost always be one or two areas somewhere which are extremely small but which contain a large quantity and therefore need a sizeable symbol. Once again the most satisfactory solution is to use the symbol sizes which the rest of the map dictates and accept overlapping as inevitable. When Fig. 25c was being worked out the unusual elongated form of the County Borough of Southport presented a problem of this kind. As an important centre of 84,000 people a circular symbol was needed, but this would have left two 'tails' at either side completely empty. Unfortunately, the circle for Southport did not displace elsewhere any other dots which might have filled these areas and to avoid the blanks on the map the method was modified slightly by cutting down the size of the symbol to 80,000 and distributing the last 4,000 in the form of 16 dots over the remainder of the area.

Devising a scale of symbol-sizes to suit a wide variety of values is not an easy task and an effective method of testing any suggested scale can be of considerable assistance. One such test is to try out the sizes envisaged on representatives of large, medium and small values and on values occurring in large, medium and small areas, avoiding extreme cases. If a reasonable fit is obtained in these six cases the scale will probably not give rise to serious difficulties, although unusual combinations of value and area may still present the odd problem.

Yet another example of the occurrence of 'awkward' values may be revealed when a dispersal graph has been drawn to determine the grouping of values for a shading map. It may be that the graph reveals well-established and narrowly defined groups generally, but with one or two values lying rather isolated between groups. The usefulness of the group in categorising sizes might be considerably weakened if it had to be extended very considerably to accommodate these isolated cases and there seems to be no reason why the group limits cannot be defined to exclude these exceptional areas; these could still be shaded in accordance with the most similar group, but marked conspicuously with an additional symbol, such as an asterisk, to indicate 'Exceptional value—not falling within the given limits of the group but so coloured because it most nearly approximates to this type'.

It will be apparent by now that the rendering of statistics into pictorial form is far from being a simple procedure, involving as it does fundamental decisions on techniques and the surmounting of difficulties inherent in the statistical material itself. More than this it involves a good deal of tedium also, for there may be long calculations needed before the method can begin and the actual plotting of the information on paper is usually a laborious and meticulous job. With as many and varied difficulties as these to be overcome it is easy to believe that they are the whole problem and there is nothing more to be considered. Unfortunately, this is not so. The *successful* presentation of a series of statistics does not end when they are committed to paper; there is a final link in the chain yet to be made—namely, the satisfactory use of the map by an observer. Few aspects of statistical presentation are more neglected than this, so much so that one feels bound to conclude that in many cases the possible difficulties of the map user have scarcely entered the draughtsman's mind and this important question of *legibility*, which has been touched upon earlier in this book, clearly demands rather more consideration here.

It is most important that when statistics are presented cartographically the resultant map should be capable of giving back to its user after a minimum of inspection and effort a clear indication of the information it was designed to carry and the main points it has to make. In the vast majority of cases this message, and the portrayal of quantities on the map, is made through the medium of abstract symbols, such as circles, bars, types of shading or a scatter of dots, which will often have been designed in such a way that they bear a distinct proportional relationship to the quantities represented. The ability of the map user to judge the significance of the size or arrangement of such symbols is therefore an important link in the chain of transferring messages from the map to its user; and the continued use of these geometrical devices seems to presuppose that many cartographers are quite satisfied that the average map user is possessed of sufficient ability to enable him to appreciate their implications. With this opinion the author disagrees. He has long sustained considerable doubts concerning ordinary people's abilities in this field and to test the validity of this belief conducted on students in the Department of Geography at the University of Leeds, an experiment which took the form outlined below.

Seven common methods of representing quantitative statistics were tested—namely, proportional bars, squares, circles and spheres, pie graphs, dots and proportional shading. For each of these methods a large card 23 in. × 18 in. was prepared on which were displayed ten values (hereafter referred to as 'quantities') and the cards were successively exhibited for a period of about four minutes to the students who were told the value of the smallest quantity on the card and asked to estimate the remaining nine. Exposure of each card was prefaced by a very brief explanation of the method involved. A second exercise was derived from the same cards by presenting the values of the smallest and largest quantities and estimating the intervening eight. To provide a different set of values from those of the first exercise the numbers involved were multiplied by a constant and, as over half an hour elapsed between the first exercise and the second, there seems little reason to believe that the second exercise was influenced by any memory of estimations made during the first. A reproduction of the cards and values used is given in Fig. 27. The experiment was tried with two separate classes, one of 20 second-year students studying for General Degrees, the other of 24 first-year students studying for an Honours Degree in Geography; the time allowances which had proved necessary for the first class were automatically imposed upon the second.

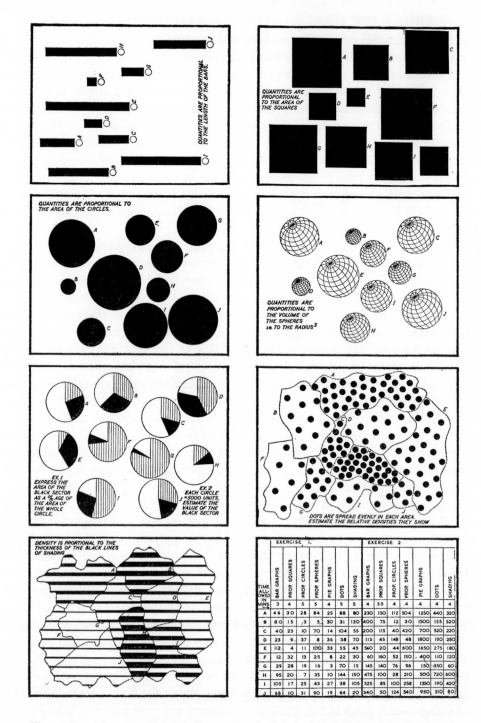

Fig. 27. Reproductions of the Cards used in the Experiment to Test Powers of Estimation. The actual values represented are given in the bottom right-hand rectangle.

The results obtained from the exercise (shown diagrammatically in Fig. 28) are most interesting, particularly in the close similarity which occurs between the answers from the two quite separate classes. All estimates for the quantities in each method have been classified as either correct or falling into one of five classes of error, the error being expressed as a percentage of the true value of the quantity which was being estimated. The percentage of the total estimates for each method which fall into the various classes of error are differently shaded and can be read on a central vertical scale. Blanks, caused by incomplete entries, are also recorded.

Fig. 28. The Results of the Experiment, showing the percentage of errors of different sizes obtained from each method.

The most outstanding feature in the results of the first exercise is the magnitude of the errors involved. Errors of ±20% and more are quite common, applying to never less than 24% of the estimates made (in pie graphs) and rising to as much as almost 80% of the total (in spheres). Quite a large proportion of the entries were in error by values ranging from ±40% to 100% or more. The best results in the experiment are noticeably those relating to linear estimation, i.e. bars, proportional shading and pie graphs[1] where half or more of the estimates were within ±20% of the correct answer. Proportional squares and circles proved more difficult of estimation; circles generally produced the less accurate results, although it should be noted that variations between the two classes in the accuracy of the estimation of circles in the first exercise provides the only instance of marked difference in the order of magnitude of the results obtained from the two separate sources. Proportional spheres proved

[1] Pie graphs involve linear estimation if the length of the arc bounding the sector is considered.

quite hopeless, the really large errors involved[1] indicating that the implications of the method were far beyond the comprehension of many students; on the other hand the results from dots, where relative 'blackness' had to be estimated proved much better than expected, about two-fifths of the estimates falling within ±20% of the correct value.

The second exercise showed that in the new conditions of estimation the *relative* accuracies of the various methods remained very little changed, but individual estimates were markedly better. Nevertheless, a sizeable proportion of the estimates was still grossly inaccurate and it is noteworthy that in most methods about a third of the estimates err by more than ±20% and the results for dots and pie graphs were scarcely improved at all.

It may be claimed that these inaccuracies were only to be expected. We are not accustomed to making fine estimates of length or size and certainly not to thinking in terms of the squares (squares and circles) and cubes (spheres) of numbers. If we do not know the cube of 6 or the difference between 7^2 and 13^2 we are hardly likely to recognise it very clearly when it is presented to us graphically, and it is precisely for this reason, of course, that graduated scales or 'sample' scales are added to statistical maps where these methods are in use. The absence of such a scale on the cards used in the experiment was one of the important differences between the experimental conditions and normal usage of a statistical map, but unfortunately the detailed results of the exercise also cast some doubts on the usefulness of these scales as aids to *visual* estimation. An outstanding feature of the estimates was that in more than half of the results the quantities were not even placed in their *correct order* of magnitude. Difficulty appeared to be encountered wherever differentiation was required between quantities which differed by 10% or less *and which were widely separated*. Similar cases where the quantities were adjacent caused little difficulty, but this does not hold out much hope that accurate estimates will be made by visual comparison against a scale which may often be at the other end of a sizeable map. Naturally, comparison by measurement could be made, but if many values had to be so treated the general efficiency of the map could only be considered as very small.

The nature of the experiment does not render it entirely immune from criticism if it is to be used as a basis for drawing conclusions with far-reaching implications. The number of students tested was small and the processes involved were not strictly those encountered in using a well-drawn statistical map with a good scale for comparison. On the other hand it is unlikely that the *average* user will spend almost five minutes perusing one statistical map (and one which contained no more than ten quantities at that) in an attempt to analyse its quantitative relationships alone, and this tends to offset the more difficult process of unaided estimation which was required. The results of the experiment on a general level cannot be gainsaid. Here were 44 persons (and there is no reason to believe they were abnormal in this respect) who experienced very real difficulty in estimating and differentiating quantities, two processes which they are frequently required to do when using statistical maps.

This result confirms the impression that there exists a very genuine dilemma for the map designer, whose task is not merely to translate statistics into a cartographic technique but to translate them into the mind of the user *via* an easily legible cartographic technique. There

---

[1] The worst was more than 900% in error and there were many more estimates well over 200% out.

arises in this connection the unfortunate paradox that the mathematical accuracy and tedious preparation of the cartographer's portrayal is matched against the comparatively inaccurate estimates and brief perusal of the average map user.

It would not be stretching the point too far to say that, on balance, a clear indication of quantity is therefore more essential than *strict* mathematical accuracy, and fortunately

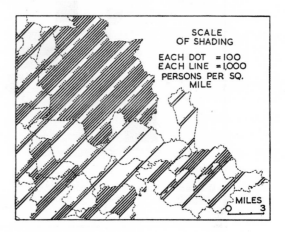

POPULATION DENSITY IN URBAN LOCAL GOVERNMENT AREAS IN THE CENTRAL WEST RIDING, 1951

POPULATION COMPOSITION IN URBAN LOCAL GOVERNMENT AREAS IN THE CENTRAL WEST RIDING, 1951

Fig. 29. Two methods rendered more legible by means of altered presentation. In the upper portion of the figure solid shading (*left*) is replaced by lines and dots (*right*) which are easily counted to obtain the required density. In the lower portion pie graphs are improved by adding a scale of *quantity* around the circumference of each circle. The lower right-hand diagram illustrates a simple way of adding such a scale using a table of chords. *Source:* Registrar-General, *Census of England and Wales, 1951,* County Volume, Yorkshire (West Riding); London (H.M.S.O.), 1954.

Fig. 30.

Switzerland—Populations of the Main Urban Centres, 1958. The two maps contrast the informative nature of a figure symbol (Fig. 30B) with the less helpful geometrical shapes (as in Fig. 30A). *Source:* Eidgenössischen Statistischen Amt, *Statistisches Jahrbuch der Schweiz, 1959/60, Basle, 1960.*

this clear indication is not difficult to achieve. A single small figure indicating the actual value written unobtrusively against a proportional symbol suffices at once to augment its usefulness (see for example Fig. 25C (p. 80)), and other methods can be redrawn in such a way that they become more legible. Scales can be added easily to devices such as proportional bars (see Fig. 13B (p. 38)), and Fig. 29 shows the same idea adapted to pie graphs and a proportional shading technique which has been redrawn, solid bands of shading being replaced by a pattern composed of lines and dots so that values may be more easily read off.

It is rather unusual, when one considers that statistical maps are designed to convey quantities to the eye, that numbers themselves have met with little use as proportional symbols. In this respect their more complex shapes, with consequent difficulties in drawing, have probably told against them, but there seems no other reason why they could not sometimes replace with great advantage the simpler geometrical symbols such as the square and circle which are so frequently employed. Fig. 30 illustrates a successful example. The figures in the lower diagram fit exactly into the squares drawn in the upper one so that the effect of distribution and of relative values remains completely unaltered whilst the lower drawing has the inestimable benefit of presenting a clear and unequivocal statement of fact without any necessity for reference to a scale line. Where statistics relating to quantity within a given area are being plotted there is the additional advantage that the figure symbol with no rigid perimeter seems to belong to the whole area; the geometrical symbol hints at concentration in one point, which is frequently not the case.

Of course it is true that all these adaptations of common techniques involve more work for the cartographer, but this is after all his job and there is at least the certainty that his efforts will be rewarded by increased legibility of the map. The improved techniques are not always as tedious as might be imagined. The numbers in Fig. 30 were easily fitted into their squares by using a rectangular type of figure, the thicknesses of the lines being automatically obtained from a pair of proportional dividers set at about 5:1; a scale of chords helps in drawing a circumferential scale for pie graphs (see Fig. 29) and this scale, when completed, may obviate the need for angular calculations as well. In Fig. 30 even representation by seven or eight sizes of 'UNO' stencilled numbers would produce an impression as useful as that obtained from squares or circles.

An interesting by-product of these more vivid methods is that continued use of the maps will often result in quite involuntary memorising of some of the more important figures found there. Indeed it may very well be true that the effect of repeatedly seeing the relevant information, even when portrayed in an entirely non-proportional manner as in Fig. 31 which is based on a page in a children's school atlas, will ultimately produce a far more real appreciation of the figures and their significance than would the same information represented by proportional geometrical symbols alone. By all means let us have proportional symbols to thrust home to the user the dominant themes on any map or diagram, but let us be sure that if it is at all possible there is equally accessible information on actual quantities as well.

Once this theme is established it is surprising how widely its ramifications can proceed. Fig. 32 shows an unusual adaptation of this idea applied to the problem of layer tinting to depict relief, the 'shading' density being derived from a printed indication of altitude seen against various backgrounds; and in Fig. 33 which illustrates a Turkish stamp issued to

Fig. 31. Part of North-west Europe, showing the populations of the principal urban centres. It seems probable that continued usage of maps with simple informative symbols of the type shown here will result in quicker and fuller appreciation of the relative size of the places shown than would the more frequently employed proportional geometrical symbols. *Source:* This figure is a slightly modified version of a page in the *All Essentials School Atlas*, published by W. and A. K. Johnston and G. W. Bacon, Ltd., Edinburgh.

Fig. 32. A New Form of Layer Tinting for Relief Maps. The incorporation of numerical designs into the shading obviates the need to refer to a key—a decided advantage where quick map-reading is essential. *Source:* A.M.S. Bulletins, No. 11, September 1944.

attract attention to a national census the message is conveyed by the figures, suitably drawn, far more vividly than it could have been by any other method. In this case the simple and direct appeal of figures instead of abstract symbols was particularly apt where a very wide public had to be reached.

Legibility of statistical maps has, of course, other facets besides the appreciation of quantitative data, but since these may generally be considered as part of the wider subject of general map design, as opposed to map techniques, they are reserved for the next chapter.

Fig. 33. A Turkish Postage Stamp issued to Publicise an Impending Census. The use of figures, rather than symbols or graphs, brings home the message of increasing population more forcefully to a wide public.

CHAPTER FIVE

General Aspects of Map Design

EVERY really good statistical map is, to some extent, an artistic creation. In common with many other devices which are used to put over or 'sell' certain ideas to a wide public, a statistical map needs 'eye-appeal' to stimulate interest and this will derive as much from good use of colour, sensible arrangement and design of components, and neat draughtsmanship, as from careful attention to statistical material and available techniques. There are very few designs for the presentation of statistics which cannot be improved by attention to the 'artistic' elements of their composition, and the purpose of this chapter is to give a brief guide to some of the more general and easily appreciated rules which govern this aspect of the work.

Naturally, in a book of this kind it is impossible to give a prolonged exposition either of the principles of artistic layout and design or of the techniques of draughtsmanship; it is quite feasible, however, to introduce the statistical cartographer to the most easily assimilated aspects of both, perhaps stimulating his interest sufficiently to pursue the matter elsewhere or encouraging him to develop the habit of observing these aspects in the many maps and diagrams which he will encounter from day to day. There is no better teacher than critical observation of the work of others, and the habit of making a mental note of a particularly attractive colour combination, layout or general design offers one of the quickest means of acquiring experience and judgement in these matters. The 'artistic' elements of design can be divided into two rather dissimilar sections—namely, general layout and design and the actual drawing of the map; in this chapter the two sections will be treated separately and in that order.

The first of these is no stranger here, for observations which could sensibly be included under the heading of general layout and design have been made from time to time. We have already met the unfortunate malady of 'statistical indigestion', for example, and its counterpart statistical congestion can be equally troublesome. The temptation to overload statistical maps is understandably very great. For various reasons, such as cost or space, they may have to be limited in number so that it appears necessary for one map to serve more than one basic purpose. At times like these it is worth while remembering that *the simpler the map the clearer it will be,* and that two simple and separate maps may each show clearly what would be only a confused jumble if combined into one. Furthermore, it is not always necessary for this splitting of the presentation to occupy more space than a combined map as simpler distributions may be shown at a smaller scale than would be necessary to maintain clarity for more complicated patterns. A good example of a type of 'combined' map which frequently fails in its object is the dot map on which two *intermixed* distributions are shown, using dots of different colour or shape. Plotted separately, each distribution would give the observer a clear picture; but on a combined map this degenerates into a vague impression that the two distributions are thoroughly intermixed. Even if the original aim was to show interrelationships between these distributions it is open to speculation whether this could not be achieved more successfully by *mental* fusion of a clear impression of the essentials of two separate distributions, rather than relying on imperfect appreciation of *visual* fusion of the two on the same map.

It is not impossible, however, to make one map serve two purposes; indeed it may sometimes be a positive advantage to do so. Where statistics relate to areas, for example, two aspects of the same situation can usually be accommodated on one map, saving space and work and giving convenient juxtaposition of complementary aspects of the situation. Fig. 34 illustrates an example of this and it will be seen that the combination is one of a *quantitative* aspect of the distribution which can be shown by a single symbol for each area, plus a more *relative* aspect where figures can be expressed as a percentage, density, ratio or in some other form suitable for portrayal by means of a shading technique. Point symbol and shaded background rarely interfere with one another and both distributions can be viewed separately or an attempt can be made to appreciate the combined implications of the two.

The idea of *attempting* to appreciate the combined implication is used deliberately in the last paragraph, for yet another fundamental rule of statistical cartography is the recognition of the observer's limitations in this respect. Too much of the deduction of inter-relationships or change should never be left to the map user to perform and if such correlations or changes are really important they will always merit separate representation, rather than being entrusted to chance recognition. Occasionally this can be accomplished by modifying the design of the maps, e.g. where a series of maps shows a city's physical growth the additional growth in each inter-map period could be differentially coloured, but where changes are more complex, such as variations in production at a number of units or changes in population distribution within a region, the only really safe course is to map this change separately.

Too much unnecessary background detail is yet another factor which may confuse or obscure the message of a map. Unnecessary background information will inevitably detract attention from the important main distributions, and features such as rivers, towns, names and boundaries not directly related to the work in hand should be eliminated or kept to a minimum. This minimum may, however, be made to serve a very useful purpose by acting as a 'geographical framework' to the main subject of the map, forming a guide to position and offering useful 'pegs' on to which may be hung less familiar aspects of the distribution. In this connection it is always wise to ensure that where places are referred to in any text which is illustrated by maps, those places are also *marked* on the maps. Few features can be more irritating than finding that full appreciation of a text is rendered impossible because additional atlas maps are not to hand. Any place so marked can be regarded as of special interest and there is no need to add all places of equivalent status merely for the sake of consistency.

Fig. 34. Two Aspects of Industrial Development in Britain, 1960-1, shown on the same map. The two methods employed—quantitative symbol and shaded background—do not conflict with one another. *Source: Local Employment Act, 1960: First Annual Report by the Board of Trade*: London (H.M.S.O.), 1961.

Attention to points of detail will often improve a map as much as will observation of the broad principles of design just described. For example, various types of shading or symbol may be designed so that they have widely differing visual appeal and dominance and this potential variation between 'dominant' and 'less significant' devices may often be used to give differential emphasis to points made on a map, or to clarify a confused situation. Fig. 35 illustrates this aspect of several designs for shading and symbols. Particularly outstanding are solid colour (especially when used as the final stage in a range of shading), bold stripes and chequerboards so that areas treated in this way can readily be expected to dominate the finished map. Ideas such as this have been freely employed in designing the illustrations for this book. Thus in Fig. 10 (p. 32) an important contrast had to be made between the concentration on short-distance sites in the conurbation towns and longer distance solutions for Inner London and Birmingham; the use of solid colour and chequerboard for these two elements and the 'playing down' of all other varieties with less clamorous shading ensured sufficient emphasis being given to this aspect of the figures. Similarly in Fig. 18 (p. 61) bold stripes were deliberately allocated to the shading for grassland, which forms so important a proportion of land use in the Netherlands.

Fig. 35. Aspects of Symbol and Shading Design.

Shading, whether applied to areas or as a filling for symbols frequently forms so important a visual element in the appearance of maps that it is important to use designs which are both harmonious and distinctive. Certain observations on this point were made in Chapter 2, but it will not come amiss to elaborate them here. Distinctiveness is best produced by ensuring variation in *density* not simply in design, little distinction being achieved, for example, between line shadings which vary only in the *direction* of the lines. Several line shadings used together may also prove rather irritating to the eye unless there is considerable complimentary variation in density; a series of dot stipples, though difficult to produce by hand, will sometimes provide clearer contrasts and more harmonious contacts at boundary lines than will line shadings, especially if the latter are of rather an open type.

Certain circumstances will occasionally prompt the use of a shading or stipple of a particular type. Broadly speaking, shadings and stipples are either compact enough to have a definite boundary or so open as to have only vaguely defined limits (see Fig. 35), and this second type will be found particularly useful for portraying a distribution where exact boundaries are unknown. One of the most fundamental drawbacks of cartographic, as opposed to literary, description of a distribution is that the map is so much more unequivocal, finding it difficult to express transitional or ill-defined areas which may be suggested by the statistics and which could easily be described in words. Anyone who has tried to plot the exact distribution of marshy areas will appreciate how very well adapted to its purpose is the open scattering of 'tufted grass' symbols which are normally employed on topographic maps; the scatter of symbols has no absolute boundary and the cartographer is spared the embarrassment of delineating a most indefinite boundary line. Similar reasons prompted the use of open symbols for depicting the major regions shown on Fig. 12 (p. 37).

Sound principles of design should, of course, be applied to symbols as well as to shading. Where space permits it is convenient for symbols to have some representational element in their design so that reference to a key is kept to a minimum; failing this other 'logical' designs can be introduced. Thus all symbols referring to related activities might incorporate the same basic shape as in Fig. 12 where all metal industries have square symbols, wood industries round ones, mining triangular and so on. Fig. 36 shows another attempt to improve the legibility of a sketch map simply by altering the design and relative emphasis of the devices used. Particular prominence has been given to those elements which were the main concern of the map—namely, proposed modernisation and improvements, and a uniformity has been imposed upon features of all kinds which are to disappear by the incorporation of an obliterating cross into their particular symbols. The wider range of overall tone and the clearer emphasis of the main features make for a more varied and interesting map.

Sensible arrangement of components is yet another aspect of symbol and map design which has already been touched upon in Chapter 2, particularly in connection with divided rectangles and compound graphs. Wherever several components are involved it will usually be found worth while to devote some thought to their detailed arrangement, e.g. in Fig. 18 (p. 61), where pie graphs are used, the two most important elements—arable and grassland—have been placed on either side of '12 o'clock', these being the two sectors whose position in the circle is the most stable and which therefore offer easiest comparisons of important constituents over the face of the map.

If a moment's attention paid to detailed points of this sort will rarely transform a bad map into a good one, it will nevertheless offer slight but significant improvements in appearance; and the advantages of design are all the more welcome because good designs rarely demand any more time and effort than bad ones.

Interpretation of the devices used on a map is achieved through a full key or legend which must be considered an integral portion of the map. Sufficient space to accommodate this key must be allowed when the overall design of the map is being worked out, and it is often surprising how much room a full key will in fact occupy. It is, presumably, this lack of room which is responsible for the keys one occasionally meets which contain no explanation but merely a series of numbers which are themselves explained in the titling below the map. The imposition of a 'key to a key' merely provides a further barrier between the map user and the realisation of the message of the map and its use is to be deplored, particularly because it would have been unnecessary if the map had been properly designed from the beginning. In addition to the key each map should incorporate a scale of distance, and many

Fig. 36. Railway Freight Modernisation Schemes in the Sheffield Area. The two maps show the same information but use differently designed symbols. In Fig. 36A these transfer attention mainly to layout, existing stations, etc., but in Fig. 36B they focus attention on to the modernisation schemes, the real subject of the map.

cartographers are tempted to add a north point as well. This latter device is often more decorative than necessary and need not be regarded as essential unless the map departs from conventional usage and has north in some direction other than at the top of the map. A suitable title will complete the essential ancillary equipment of any map, but it should be noted that where maps are being drawn to accompany a printed text it is usual today to omit the title from the design of the map and instead to set it up in type underneath the map, along with any necessary annotation; the illustrations used in this book have all been designed in this way.

Even the best designed statistical map, incorporating a sensible basic technique and attending to the detailed points described in this chapter, will not automatically have eye-appeal, and it is important to consider how this essential aspect of visual attraction may be incorporated into the design. From an aesthetic point of view, general attention to the layout of the elements which make up the map will help. The relative positions of title, scale, key and the main body and margins of the map can sometimes be varied so that a more 'balanced' composition is achieved, but all too often there is little opportunity for variation, basic shapes being such that these devices have to be restricted to those parts of the map which are not otherwise needed. In practice a much more widely applicable method of contributing eye-appeal will be found in the sensible use of colour.

Few people are able to restrain their curiosity when their eye chances on some attractive, vividly coloured map, and though upon examination the subject matter may prove insufficient to retain their attention the fact remains that initially this was not a prime consideration and their attention *was* attracted. Few cartographers could ask for more than this chance of catching the eye of the public and such a potential in the use of colour obviously demands exploitation to the full. The many brightly coloured maps which one often encounters today indicate a widespread awareness of this amongst modern map-publishers and provide a welcome change from the weakly uninteresting cream, pale pinks and pale blues so often encountered in 'Commerical Atlases' of thirty years or so ago.

Whilst it would not be practicable here to enter into a prolonged consideration of the principles of colour harmony or the means of determining striking and pleasing colour combinations, a few very elementary rules can be described. In general it will be found advisable not to use too many different colours on any one map; the greater the number of colours the more difficult will it be to ensure that all of them exist harmoniously side by side, as they will almost certainly have to do somewhere on the face of the map. Similarly, in maps for which the bulk of the area needs colour in fairly large patches the juxtaposition of too many bright colours should be avoided, much better results being obtained from the use of only one or two bright colours with slightly muted tones for the rest of the areas.

Another common type of map is one where considerable areas of background colour are needed, against which small but important points of detail, such as symbols, have to be shown. Where this occurs it is best to have for the background a very 'tolerant' colour, such as pale yellow or pale grey, which need not be a 'flat' grey but which can incline towards blue, green or brown, for example, to harmonise with other colours used. Both of these backgrounds will carry almost all other colours without disharmony and the detail can therefore be picked out in very bright, clear colours such as scarlet, cobalt blue, medium green or of course black. Greens, blues and browns can also be used as background colours, but impose a rather narrower range for the colours of the other items, and in all instances where bright colours are needed for the detail the background should remain quite pale; increasing amounts of background colour would need darker, rather muted colours such as crimson, prussian blue or dark green for the symbols to maintain colour harmony.

 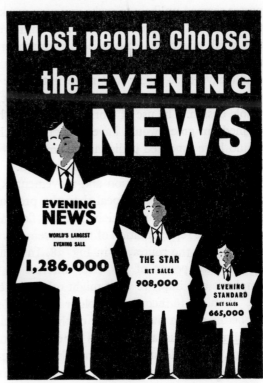

Fig. 37. Two Posters issued to publicise Newspaper Circulation. The second poster was substituted for the first because of its greater interest and eye-appeal.

Fortunately today the amateur who takes an interest in colour will find plenty of guidance all around him. Book, magazines, posters, films, interior decoration and so, all make lavish use of colour and the cartographer cannot do better than observe these critically and to take his cue from those examples he encounters which particularly strike his eye.

Colour is perhaps the most widely applicable method of adding eye-appeal to maps and diagrams, but other devices will help too. Symbols of a semi-pictorial, or even a numeral type, as in Fig. 30B (p. 90) tend to have rather more interest than simple geometrical ones and Fig. 37 illustrates how much more attractive similar information appears when displayed in a more pictorial manner. Both posters were originally printed in bright 'day-glo' colours on a black background, thus appearing quite striking to the eye, yet the second poster was substituted for the first because of the increased interest which it contained. In direct contrast to the simple, yet bold and colourful appeal of this second poster the author recently encountered a small leaflet-poster issued to encourage funds for a Diocesan Appeal. The basic device was an annular shape, similar to that of a child's 'oval' railway track, in the centre of which was a representation of a bishop's mitre; the 'oval' band had then been divided, pie-graph fashion, into segments, labelled to indicate the way in which the money would be spent, and the whole was printed in black on pale blue paper. In view of the very genuine need to arouse interest in this cause it was unfortunate that on its *visual* merits this small poster seemed unlikely to make any very marked impression. The general design was weak—the oval band was much too thin and unimpressive to act as the main part of the design and this weak effect was emphasised, if anything, by a relatively small bishop's mitre floating aimlessly in the central space; if a strong, bold circular device had been used, the segments could have been larger and more noticeable and the central space could have been small enough just to have contained the mitre which would have acted as a genuine focus for the whole design. The use of a brightly coloured background paper, say a bold yellow, turquoise or medium green would have strengthened the visual appeal of the poster still further and would have rendered it distinctive amongst the mass of church porch notices which seemed likely to form its more usual surroundings.

A feeling of animation and movement is yet another device which will add interest to a map and give more appeal than the presentation of a static picture. In this way, a map involving routes along which traffic is flowing can be improved by incorporating into the design some representation of this movement, such as arrow symbols, rather than mere bands to represent the routes, as in Fig. 38. In a rather similar way the use of three-dimensional symbols for points of *particular* interest on an otherwise two-dimensional map will add emphasis and improve what might otherwise be a very 'flat' picture.

Inability to incorporate colour into the design of a map is always frustrating, if only for no better reason than the loss of the potential eye-appeal of bright colours. Unfortunately, this limitation usually imposes other more important and fundamental difficulties into the design, not the least of which are those connected with difficulties of recognition and differentiation. An important asset of bold colours is that they remain distinctive, even where only minute areas have to be shown, in a way that different types of shading do not; and in techniques such as pie graphs which introduce several variables, often occupying quite small areas, inability to use colour can be a serious handicap. If considerations such as cost or technical difficulties should impose black-and-white-only rendering any shadings used should be designed with particular care so that they remain distinctive when applied to quite small areas. This is not always easy to achieve, but Fig. 35 incorporates a range which would be reasonably satisfactory in this respect and which would allow the use of six variables on one map without much danger of confusion.

At no time is the lack of colour more annoying than when a shading range has to be devised to accommodate both positive and negative values of the same thing. The logical choice here would be to progress from white or very pale colours around zero into stronger shades of, say, red for increasingly positive values and blue for increasingly negative ones, and the arrangement is a very satisfactory one. Lack of colour around zero emphasises the 'nothing much happening' range of values whilst the contrast between the strong red and the recessive blue differentiates between positive and negative aspects of the higher values.

Fig. 38. 'The Fight for Eastern England.' The style of this map attempts to convey something of the animation and strife which underlay one of the greatest British Parliamentary railway 'battles'. The map is designed to enhance the 'feeling' of the implications of success by the London and York; a *series* of arrows increases animation and these penetrate to the heart of the 'target' symbols whilst others are kept on the perimeter.

103

In black and white this would have to be replaced by two distinct types of shading, e.g. a dot stipple and a line-shading for negative and positive values respectively, but it is difficult to ensure that the two have sufficiently different visual qualities for the negative values to come out less strongly than the positive ones. The only alternative to this is to have an increasing intensity of shading right through the scale of values, with blanks showing the lowest values of all. This makes it difficult to pick out the values around zero although this can sometimes be done by making a major change in shading type, e.g. from dots to lines, at or near that point. It is not always easy to decide which of these two courses is best suited to a given range of figures, and a great deal will depend on which particular parts of the range, if any, need accentuating; examples of both types will be found in Figs. 43A and B (p. 123).

Once considerations affecting the design of the map have been completed, there remains the practical task of actually drawing it, and it is at this point, when the final transference of the information to paper must be achieved, that many amateur cartographers feel most at a disadvantage. Consciousness of lack of ability or experience in draughtsmanship all too often leads unnecessarily to a sense of pessimism and frustration—an 'Oh! I'm no good at drawing' or 'I'm not much of an artist' feeling which breeds defeatism, slap-dash work and lack of interest. Naturally the amateur cannot expect to produce work which will compare with that of a skilled craftsman who has been doing the job for years, but on the other hand simple draughtsmanship techniques are not difficult to learn. If the amateur cartographer will not set his sights too high and is prepared to aim at relatively simple, bold results incorporating only a minimum of the more sophisticated techniques (e.g. varied lettering or fine line work) and above all is prepared to take a little time and trouble there is no reason why quite passable results should not be obtained. Contrary to popular belief most draughtsmen are made, not born; their skill is largely acquired by patience and prolonged experience and many people could become much more adequate draughtsmen if they were prepared to accept each new piece of work as yet another opportunity to acquire this skill, rather than as another job to be completed as quickly as possible.

In drawing, as in many other activities, it is true to say that the best results are usually achieved with the best tools for the job and good equipment will always repay the expenditure which it involves. Nevertheless, the person who finds himself required only occasionally to undertake cartographic work will not wish to purchase a very wide range of expensive equipment, and fortunately there is no need for him to do so. Few of the items needed for ordinary draughtsmanship are costly and many of the more expensive ones can often be borrowed or improvised. A good example of an item of equipment of this type is a drawing board which, if available, will form a stable, level and portable base for the work. Alternatively, any large, flat piece of board or plywood, such as a large baking board, will serve the same purpose, provided that it is thick enough, and has one edge straight enough to allow a T-square to be used against it.

A T-square and its complements—a pair of 30°/60° and 45° set squares *are* essential items of equipment for any would-be draughtsman. The T-square should be used against the left-hand edge of the board so that when moved up and down along this edge it can be used to draw horizontal lines in any position. The set squares are used principally to draw vertical lines (and also lines at 30°, 45° and 60° to the horizontal) by moving them along the top edge of the T-square as shown in Fig. 39. It is worth while noting that vertical lines are not drawn by using the T-square along the top edge of the board, for few boards, even of the true drawing-board type, are square enough to give two sets of lines exactly at right angles; it will be obvious that for drawings of any size demanding many vertical lines a pair of large set-squares will be much more convenient than very small ones. The amateur draughtsman will rarely find much use for the rather expensive adjustable type of set-square which can be set to draw lines at any angle to the horizontal.

Fig. 39. The use of T-square and set-squares with a drawing-board and (*below*) three types of pen commonly employed in cartography: (*left to right*) a 'UNO' lettering pen, a ruling pen, and a dotting pen.

Of the remaining items needed for the construction of maps none is expensive or difficult to obtain. A good 12-in. ruler, preferably with $\frac{1}{10}$ths and centimetres marked along the full length, a relatively hard pencil, say 2H, for construction lines, a good quality soft rubber, a small protractor and a pair of compasses will suffice for most work. The hard pencil should be used *lightly* to produce fine construction lines easily erased later, but if used in a rather 'heavy-handed' fashion it may produce small grooves in the paper which are almost impossible to remove completely. Compasses probably offer a wider choice than any of the items of equipment described so far, but the author has found that the simple 'schoolboy' type in cast brass or alloy is usually perfectly satisfactory. In this type the two limbs are joined at the top by a small nut and bolt which can be kept permanently tightened to prevent slipping whilst the pencil 'socket', which is tightened by a threaded brass ring, is generous enough in size to accommodate not only pencils but most types of penholders too, so that the compasses can be used for ink as well as pencil. The main disadvantage of this type of compass for ink work is that it is not possible always to have the writing arm meeting the paper at right angles; more expensive types of compass have the useful refinement of having the lower portion of the writing arm hinged to allow this right-angled contact with the paper to be maintained.

For drawing irregular curves the relevant portions of one or more French curves may be used. These are not expensive and can be bought either singly or in sets. As with set-squares it is sensible to obtain them with a bevelled edge for use with ink as well as pencil. The more elaborate devices for drawing irregular curves will rarely give the amateur draughtsman sufficient use to justify their cost.

The choice of a suitable medium on which to draw the finished map is apt to concern the amateur draughtsman rather less than his equipment or lack of it, yet the choice can be an important one and since most types of paper are cheap enough this is one item in the work where it is easy to obtain the best quality possible. Heavy quality cartridge paper is the medium which most people find both readily available and practicable. The great advantage of the heavier quality papers is that they provide a smoother and tougher surface on which to work and generally withstand wetting, e.g. if water colours are used, more successfully than the cheaper, thinner ones. Their tough surface will be particularly appreciated in facilitating the erasure of any mistakes which cannot be removed by a ordinary rubber (see below).

If the drawing has to be prepared on a transparent medium, for example as an overlay, the usual choice is a good quality strong tracing paper. This has the advantage of being readily available and of allowing easy erasure by scraping, but it is unfortunately quite unsuited to wetting, which causes troublesome crinkling and is very liable to change its size and shape slightly but noticeably with changes in humidity so that overlays of any size frequently have only a poor quality fit after a time. Avoidance of this stretching can be achieved by drawing on one of the several plastic films which are available, such as 'Ethulon' and 'Koda-trace', though these have the disadvantages of being much less widely obtainable, more expensive and equally unsuited to colour. Such films usually have one shiny side and one matt side, the latter being used for drawing on, but even so the surface may need powdering with French chalk, and Indian ink is liable to flake off if heavily applied; drawing on such a surface needs rather more skill than on cartridge or normal tracing paper. Tracing linen, often used in drawing offices because of its durability in handling, is a similar, difficult medium for the amateur and its use is normally unnecessary for map work.

The medium chosen must be fixed to the drawing board or drawing surface. The amateur is inclined to use drawing pins, which are often at hand, but these spoil both the surface of the drawing and the board and may occasionally foul drawing implements too. The professional draughtsman almost always uses draughting tape, a variety of adhesive paper tape so treated that it can be pulled away from both board and drawing without damaging either. Ordinary transparent cellulose tape should *not* be substituted as almost inevitably it will bring away the surface of the paper if attempts are made to remove it.

Most amateur cartographers are prepared to construct maps in pencil, but have far more misgivings about the final processes of inking in or colouring these. Admittedly liquid media need somewhat more skill and are more difficult to correct if mistakes are made, but even so many cartographers could improve their performance by the application of little more than an increased amount of care and patience, and with only a small amount of practice quite good results can be obtained.

Of all the liquid 'finishing' media Indian inks are the most commonly used, their application to the paper usually being made with some form of pen. These range from pens of the normal 'nib type', such as a crow quill, to pens with special nibs for making particular shapes or lines, e.g. dotting pens, and items such as ruling and lettering pens which are rather different types of devices. The crow quill was formerly much used for map work because of its ability to draw a fine line, greatly curved if necessary, but it is not an easy instrument to use, particularly with regard to maintaining consistency of width of line. Like all pens of the 'nib type' it functions more satisfactorily if the ink is applied with a dropper only to the *underside* of the nib and it needs frequent wiping, for Indian ink dries quickly at room temperature, clogging the pen and making thick lines.

For much of the line work on maps and drawings the professional draughtsman will use a 'ruling pen' which has a 'nib' made of two parallel blades (see Fig. 39) between which ink is placed by means of a dropper. The distance between the blades can be adjusted so that the pens will rule lines of any thickness from very fine indeed to about $\frac{1}{16}$th of an inch wide. Ruling pens are not expensive nor particularly difficult to use, at least for straight lines, but they do need to be kept absolutely clean if they are to function successfully, and need sharpening from time to time if they are in constant use. Very sharply curved lines, such as boundaries or rivers, are not so easily drawn with the ordinary ruling pen, although a version known as a 'contour pen' in which the nib is mounted on a swivel to facilitate turning corners is sometimes used. Most amateurs will find, however, that one of the pens supplied for stencil lettering is much easier to use not only for this type of line but also for most line work in cartography. In pens of this sort (see Fig. 39) the ink is contained in a cylindrical or conical reservoir and is fed to the paper through a tube which varies in diameter according to the size of the pen. Though supplied principally for lettering these pens are extensively used for line work in cartography today, so much so that they have in many cases almost superseded the crow quill and ruling pen for ordinary work. A range of tube sizes from very small to $\frac{3}{16}$th of an inch or so in diameter makes it possible to draw lines of a wide range of width; the constant flow of ink from the reservoir produces a consistent line and the tubular 'nib' makes rapid movement in any direction quite easy. Advantages such as this, together with their usefulness for lettering, make a limited range of pens of this kind a sound investment.

Lettering, formerly the bane of the amateur cartographer, need cause little difficulty today. Technical aids, which are freely available, render it extremely easy for him to produce neat, legible lettering in many sizes and styles which, though they may occasionally lack the individuality and subtlety of hand-produced lettering, are capable of satisfying all but the most fastidious tastes. For lettering of this type stencils are normally used, the most widely encountered being those supplied under the trade names of 'UNO' and 'Leroy'. These show considerable variety in size and some in style, e.g. upright, sloping, 'architectural' (i.e. with rather narrower letters than normal) as well as upper and lower case of course. In addition a further range of stencils is available for drawing commonly encountered symbols, either of various types, e.g. for electrical drawings, or of the same type in a graduated range of sizes, e.g. circles, squares or triangles.

When lettering with these stencils the draughtsman need only be concerned with ensuring that the correct spacing is obtained between the letters, the stencils being normally used with the lower edge resting on a T-square or straight-edge so that they can be moved about laterally to bring the next letter into its required position.

If stencils are not available, lettering may have to be done by hand and in this case most amateurs would benefit by the generous provision of guide lines and the use of a set-square to ensure that all 'uprights' are truly vertical or slope at the same angle if an italic style is used. Variations in style in freehand lettering can be produced by the use of different shaped nibs, of which a wide range is available. Those supplied under the trade name of 'Pelikan Graphos' include nibs to produce a comprehensive range of styles and in Britain cards of nibs of different sizes to produce a particular type of lettering and sold by the firm of Wm. Mitchell are frequently seen in stationers' shops. If attempts at freehand lettering prove unsatisfactory another solution is to type the necessary names on gummed paper, cut them out and stick them firmly to the map. This solution will, of course, place all names on the map in a white 'window' which may or may not be an advantage; the results may furthermore be rather mechanical in appearance, but this is probably to be preferred to a map rendered untidy by poor hand-lettering.

For larger lettering or work in a wider variety of styles alphabets can now be obtained with adhesive letters supplied on cellulose sheets, the letters being removed as required and fixed to the drawing. The range of size and style, e.g. that produced by 'Letraset', is indeed truly remarkable, although availability is not always particularly widespread and cost may be high unless a considerable amount of work is being undertaken to give maximum use of the alphabets supplied. In a similar fashion a multitude of shadings, stipples, symbols and other devices are all available ready printed on adhesive transparent sheets. If these are cut to shape and then applied to the relevant portions of the map much tedious work can be avoided. As with letters, cost will be more reasonable for a number of maps than for an isolated example where sheets of several patterns might be needed though each one would be very little used. It must be admitted that both adhesive letters and patterns enhance the appearance of the map by producing a rather 'professional' appearance, especially with devices such as even stipples which are difficult and tedious to produce by hand over large areas. On the other hand, hand-drawn shading can be quite effective and satisfactory, provided that sufficient care is taken to draw guide lines in first in the manner already described in Chapter 2.

Perhaps one of the main reasons for the amateur's mistrust of liquid media, as opposed to pencil, arises from the greater difficulty in correcting any mistakes which may be made. Naturally, mistakes are better avoided altogether, but even the professional draughtsman will err occasionally and the important factor is not so much not to make mistakes as to know how to correct them when they are made. Any mistakes which will not respond to an ordinary eraser are usually removed by scraping the ink or colour off the surface of the paper by means of a sharp, straight edge such as a razor blade scraped along the paper itself or at a very small angle to the surface; if the blade is held at a larger angle the end of the cutting edge will tend to dig in, breaking through the working surface of the paper and roughening the looser fibres underneath. With cheap, thin papers which have little working surface this scraping process can only be used with caution, but with harder, thicker paper, or on tracing paper, a surprising amount of erasing is possible by this means, and on the very best quality paper such as hand-made Whatman or on Bristol Board[1] the surface is hardly affected. After erasing, it is usual to smooth out any roughness which may be present by rubbing the erased portion with some hard, smooth object. Most professional draughtsmen carry a small piece

[1] A type of thin, white card with a very smooth surface, often used where a very durable drawing is required.

of bone for this purpose, but other surfaces, e.g. a rounded portion of a perfectly smooth, plastic penholder, can be substituted.

Really drastic mistakes such as a very large blot or smear or an incorrectly drawn section too large to erase satisfactorily may need more serious treatment if the whole map is not to be redrawn. The drawing should be laid on a smooth surface with a piece of the same paper placed underneath the area which contains the mistake; this area should then be cut out of the map with a very sharp knife, ensuring that the blade penetrates cleanly *both* thicknesses of paper. If the spoilt portion is now removed a blank piece of the same material, and of exactly the right shape, is available to fill the hole and can be held in place by adhesive tape on the back of the map. For drawings which are to be reproduced as line blocks to accompany text, erasure is relatively easy, for the mistakes can simply be painted out with an opaque white substance known as 'process white'. Process white does not show up when the drawing is photographed in the making of the line-block and the obliterated error is entirely invisible on the finished representation.

Whilst Indian inks are perfectly suitable for coloured line work their waterproof quality makes them difficult to apply evenly over large areas and, for this purpose, some other colouring medium must be used. Large areas of pale colour can be satisfactorily achieved by using water colours or stick inks made up with water and generously applied with a large brush, but unfortunately it is not easy for the amateur to imitate the large areas of solid *bright* colours which are responsible for much of the attractiveness and eye-appeal of printed maps and diagrams. The lithographic process which is normally used in printing these maps is particularly adapted to this kind of effect, but has no easy parallel in 'hand' methods of applying colour. Poster colour will be found to be the most suitable medium for producing large areas of opaque bright colour and though the results are usually perfectly satisfactory, most people find it a slow medium in which to work and one which is apt to flake off if applied too heavily and roughly handled afterwards. For slightly less dense patches of colour a wide range of non-waterproof inks is available. Their non-waterproof nature makes them rather easier to apply evenly over large areas than Indian ink, but it is notoriously more difficult to achieve satisfactory results with some colours than others and a trial run on a piece of scrap paper is often advisable before applying the colour to the main map. Because these non-water-proof inks are not opaque all construction lines and unwanted detail must be removed before they are applied.

It is unfortunate that many people regard crayon as rather a 'childish' or second-rate colouring medium. Although not much used by the professional draughtsman for his finished work it has several advantages for the amateur. Its 'pencil' nature gives confidence, it is quick to use and is capable of producing a wide range of colour intensity, matching that of both poster and water colours combined, as well as being adapted to producing 'shading-off' or gradation in colour which is not easily achieved by the amateur in any other medium. The greatest difficulty with crayon arises when large areas have to be shaded evenly, but the secret here is to employ a good quality crayon with a *soft* lead and work gradually over the area to be covered with a gentle circular motion, treating relatively small areas at a time. Intensity of colour over large areas is more uniformly achieved by producing a lighter colour first and going over the area again rather than trying to build up the full intensity from the beginning. Shading with a side-to-side motion, which is the method normally adopted by amateurs, will tend to produce variations in intensity, making it difficult to obtain the evenness of tone which is desired. If several shades of one colour are needed, e.g. in a graduated range of shading, it is perhaps best to use solid colour only for the highest value and obtain the other shades by building up colour intensity with line shading; it is not easy to maintain several recognisably distinct shades of *solid* colour, using the same crayon for each. It is probably true to say that if the finished map is relatively small the amateur can achieve speedier and more striking results working with crayon than with most other coloured media, but unfortunately the shiny surface produced by most crayons means that ink cannot be applied successfully to a crayoned surface and any lettering must therefore be either hand-drawn in crayon or pencil, or typed and stuck on as described above.

The help and advice given in the latter part of this chapter are, quite obviously, intended for those with little experience of draughtsmanship. The simple, relatively easily acquired techniques and skills which are described here should encourage even those with little experience to attempt to produce neat, effective cartographic work, although naturally the results achieved at first will fall far short of those produced by the more experienced draughtsman who will already have encountered the different media and established his preferences amongst them. Even so it should be remembered that there is far more to a map than a neat appearance and good draughtsmanship. Good draughtsmanship, however desirable, must take its place along with attention to sources, sensible use of material, choice of method, and general design as merely one factor among many which must be incorporated into the construction of any map or diagram. On its own, however glib or professional it may appear, it will not automatically produce a good map and the person who has carefully weighed these other factors need not be hypersensitive that limitations in his draughting ability will seriously reduce the value of his work.

CHAPTER SIX

Some Worked Examples

In the foregoing chapters the essentially compound process of devising a statistical map or diagram has had to be analysed into its component parts so that a set of principles, applicable to each of these could be evolved. In practice, of course, the difficulties presented by each aspect of the situation cannot be resolved separately, but must be approached in the light of their interaction one with another if a pleasing, balanced and efficient map is to result. Using worked examples of statistical situations this chapter seeks to restore this balance and, by presenting each problem as an entity, gives to the reader a limited idea of the considerations involved in viewing such a situation 'in the round' rather than from a narrow specialised point of view.

The examples used have been chosen principally because they are illustrations of certain commonly recurring types of statistical situation (they are in fact described under 'type-headings' rather than as individual problems), but also because it is precisely these kinds of distribution which the amateur cartographer so often finds himself having to illustrate.

EXAMPLE 1. A DISTRIBUTION CONCERNED ESSENTIALLY WITH A SINGLE VARIABLE. THE DISTRIBUTION OF THE CHEMICAL INDUSTRY IN ENGLAND AND WALES, 1951 (FIG. 40)

Of all types of distribution which have to be mapped, that dealing with a single variable is perhaps the most simple and also one of the most frequently encountered. Let us take as an example an attempt to show the main features of the distribution of the chemical industry in England and Wales in 1951.

SOURCE OF INFORMATION

This must be considered first, as the information it yields will inevitably form a limiting framework to the design of the whole map. Fortunately, an excellent and complete source is available in the Industry Tables of the 1951 Census of England and Wales, the total numbers employed in 'Chemicals and Allied Trades' being given for each Local Authority area (i.e. County or Municipal Borough, Urban or Rural District). As defined in the Industrial Classification used in the Census the term 'Chemicals and Allied Trades' includes a range of activities rather wider than those which the layman often thinks of under the heading 'chemicals'. For towns of more than 50,000 population the total employed in the whole industry and in each of seven main subdivisions is given; these are (*a*) coke-ovens and by-products; (*b*) chemicals, dyes, explosives, fireworks; (*c*) pharmaceutical, toilet preparations, etc.; (*d*) paint and varnish; (*e*) soap, candles, polishes, ink, matches; (*f*) mineral oil refining; (*g*) other oils, greases, glue, etc. Unfortunately for smaller authorities the only subtotal is that for groups (*a*) and (*b*) *combined*.

ASPECTS TO BE CONSIDERED

The principal impression of the distribution of the industry throughout the country must inevitably be derived here from the variation in the distribution of workers employed in it. There is no uniform source of detailed information based on production, nor is it easy to see how one could be devised to accommodate the various end products of so wide a range of activities as those specified above. *Some way of presenting quantitative aspects of employment in the industry at the various places where it occurs is therefore a prime requirement.*

A glance at the figures suggests that other aspects might be relevant in obtaining a general picture of the industry, e.g. there is considerable variation of industry within the main industrial class and even a cursory inspection reveals that there are at least two basic types of *place* involved. These are (*a*) the 'chemical town', where chemicals form one of the main sources of employment and assume, therefore, unusual importance, and (*b*) the town where chemicals are merely one industry among many, even though the total number employed in chemicals is quite large. Contrasting examples of these are provided by Runcorn U.D., where the chemical industry provided 5,304 jobs or 44% of all employment within the Urban District, and Leeds where a slightly smaller total of 4,227 jobs in the chemical industry accounted for a relatively insignificant proportion ($1\frac{1}{2}$%) of the total employment. *Thus some means of indicating the importance of the industry in the places where it occurs would be desirable.*

GENERAL STATISTICAL CONSIDERATIONS

The territorial distribution of the industry and the range of numbers employed are both very wide indeed. Few local authorities are completely without people employed in 'chemicals', though in many cases the totals are very small, often less than 20; on the other hand the 'giants' give figures of several thousands, and totals of several hundreds are not uncommon. It seems fairly clear from this, that in a national survey of this kind which must attempt to emphasise the essentially important aspects of the distribution it would be pointless to clutter the map with many examples of places where the industry is of little importance, and after inspecting the figures in several typical localities it was decided to omit all authorities where the number employed fell below 350. This figure was decided upon quite arbitrarily, partly by the general run of the figures and partly from individual knowledge, the main aim being to ensure that no place which was known to have an important chemical works appeared to be excluded. A more precise solution to this problem could have been obtained by means of a dispersal graph, but this would have been unnecessarily tedious to prepare in view of the very large number of occurrences involved. Even so, this whittling down left some 200 or so localities to be represented and the range involved was still very wide, running from 350 jobs to more than 10,000.

To avoid the kind of statistical anomalies mentioned in Chapter 3 it was decided to amalgamate at least the figures for Manchester, Stretford and Salford; Liverpool and Bootle; Newcastle and Gateshead; and Birmingham and Smethwick. To avoid congestion and to allow the London area to stand out in its true perspective, figures for places within the Greater London Conurbation[1] were included as one unit. The great majority of the figures used related to urban authorities, which, though technically 'areas', were small enough to be reduced to and regarded as 'points' on the finished map; and for these areas it was also meaningful to express the total of chemical workers as a percentage of all employment. The remaining figures appeared to present rather more of a problem. They related to Rural Districts which were often of such a size that it would have been impossible to regard them as 'points' had it not been for the fortunate fact that in the great majority of cases it seemed likely that the figure was derived largely from only *one* major establishment which could usually be identified (e.g. the Harwell Atomic Energy Establishment obviously accounted for the great majority of the total of 2,796 'chemical jobs' in Wantage R.D.) and a point symbol located at that particular place would serve perfectly well. *The basic distribution, therefore, though technically relating to areas could in fact be treated as a series of 'point' values.* Unfortunately, with respect to *composition* the rural areas could not be dismissed so lightly. A single large works at one end of a Rural District might be so inaccessible as not to affect potential employment at the other extremities of the area, and to express 'chemical jobs' as a percentage of something which in this respect scarcely functioned as a unit seemed pointless. In many cases too, the works, though technically in Rural Districts, were, in effect, close to urban authorities and probably drew more of their workers from these towns than from the remaining parts of the same Rural District. Thus the 2,092 'chemical jobs' in Lancaster R.D. were largely concentrated at the oil refinery at Heysham, only a short distance from the towns of Morecambe and Lancaster; to express this figure as 37% of all jobs in Lancaster R.D. seems simply to refer to a fictional situation, entirely unrepresentative of conditions in Lancaster R.D. generally. *For sites in rural areas, therefore, no attempt is made to express the relative importance of employment in the chemical industries* although it can be assumed that in a rural area *any* large factory forms an extremely important local source of employment.

CHOICE OF METHOD AND DETAILS

The basic choice of method was never in doubt. With almost 200 values ranging in size from 350 to 10,000 a series of quantitative symbols was needed, either strictly proportional individually or grouped into size categories. The latter solution was decided upon principally because it was felt that with so large a number of symbols the map reader needed a certain amount of guidance with information sorted out into different degrees of importance. A dispersal graph of the values established the most suitable division points. It will be noticed that the larger categories cover a relatively wide range of values (the upper limit is frequently 50% or more in excess of the lower one), but this is almost inevitable as values on the dispersal graph 'thin out' and indeed above 4,500 occurrences become so dispersed as almost to preclude the possibility of grouping. In this last group of 'giants', which contains places all of which could be said to be amongst the main centres of the industry in the country, there is

[1] Defined in the *Census of England and Wales, 1951*, Industry Volume.

Fig. 40.
The Distribution of the Chemical Industry in England and Wales, 1951.
Source: Registrar-General, *Census of England and Wales, 1951,*
Industry Volume; London (H.M.S.O.), 1957.

indeed so wide a range that some other means of indicating quantity is needed as well. In defining a suitable size for the symbols an attempt was made to keep some aspect of the actual quantities in view, and the diameters used are in fact close to those which would have represented a value half-way between the extremes of each group if a strictly proportional symbol had been used. The series does, however, contain two marked 'steps' in symbol size—namely, between the third and fourth sizes used and between the sixth and the seventh. These are introduced partly to break up the range and make recognition easier, but principally because each marks a major change in the extent of the groups, the first three symbols covering relatively small ranges and the last one (the seventh) an extremely extended range. To cover the extended range of the seventh group all symbols also carry the actual numbers employed (in hundreds) after the name. Whilst it would have been more satisfactory to have placed this total either adjacent to, or within the actual symbol, congestion in some areas, notably South Lancashire, rendered this impossible.

Having overcome the problem involved in establishing the primary distribution the next stage was to consider how best to add to the map a second aspect, indicating the relative importance of the industry at each place. One possibility here was to shade the symbols differentially, but this was not used since a uniform solid symbol is important to give the maximum visual emphasis to the principal distribution. Instead, the idea of introducing differentially written names was adopted. Names are easily written in a number of different ways to indicate various categories, as well as serving as a useful form of identification. Not all locations shown on the map are named; in an 'all black' map these would soon fill the map and destroy the impression of the first distribution so that names are only given for those areas where more than 1,000 people are employed in the chemical industry or where the industry accounts for more than 5% of all jobs. Names in the latter group are presented in three ways, according to whether the percentage exceeds 5, 10 or 20, and in accordance with the principle established above this aspect of the figures was not presented for Rural Districts. The limits of 5, 10 and 20% were quite arbitrary and were chosen because in the majority of cases they could be determined by inspection without need for further calculations.

The possibility of introducing a third aspect on to the map to illustrate variation in the type of industry was considered, but rejected. Had colour been possible it would not have been difficult to achieve this by using the same symbols or names differentially coloured. In black and white the counterpart of this would have been differentially shaded symbols and this had already been rejected. The alternative was to incorporate information of this type in a separate inset map where different symbols (non-proportional) could have indicated towns where various branches of the industry were dominant. Unfortunately, there was room for only one inset map and it was decided to utilise this space for purposes which essentially completed the kind of information given in the main map—namely, a summary diagram which shows the general national distribution of the industry. With so many individual symbols involved it is difficult for the map user to judge precisely what the total effect of these in any one area amounts to, especially in comparison with other areas; to overcome this difficulty the inset map expresses the total employed in certain of the main concentrations as a percentage of the total employed nationally in the industry.

GENERAL CONCLUSIONS DERIVED FROM FIG. 40

(*a*) The industry is widely distributed with certain locational types commonly occurring —namely, (1) in the main conurbations and large towns and (2) in coastal localities. Three concentrations in particular stand out above all the rest. Greater London and the South Lancashire-Cheshire area each have about a quarter of the total employed nationally in the industry, and the Tyneside-Tees-side area accounts for a further 10%. Other areas are not individually important on a national scale though sizeable numbers of workers may be involved.

(*b*) Areas with over 1,000 persons employed in the industry are frequently encountered, but with the exception of the Mersey area the largest totals are usually in the big cities where the industry is *relatively* of small importance. Generally speaking, it is often in the smaller town, where numbers involved may be less than 1,000, that the chemical industry forms a substantial proportion of local employment. South Lancashire, where large numbers are employed in medium-sized towns, is exceptional and in that area chemicals account for a considerable proportion of local employment.

EXAMPLE 2. A DISTRIBUTION CONCERNED ESSENTIALLY WITH A SINGLE VARIABLE, BUT WITH MAJOR STATISTICAL COMPLICATIONS. POPULATION CHANGE IN THE NORTH RIDING OF YORKSHIRE, 1931-51 (FIG. 41)

One of the most serious defects of published statistics is that they are, at times, capable of being quite unrepresentative of a *detailed* situation. This defect was examined in broad outline in Chapter 3 where examples illustrated how the use of different bases for representing population change from 1931 to 1951 in the North Riding of Yorkshire could produce widely varying results. The end-products of this experiment were presented there in Fig. 22 (p. 72), but it was pointed out that even Fig. 22C, the best of the results, was more expedient than accurate and the further consideration of the figures which was promised at that time will now be attempted.

SOURCE OF INFORMATION

The same source will be used here as in the compilation of Fig. 22—namely, the Yorkshire East and North Ridings volume of the 1951 Census of England and Wales. This provides figures for the 1931 and 1951 populations for each administrative area, including figures for individual parishes in rural areas. Figures are given for both total population and 'population in private households' (i.e. excluding people in institutions and communal establishments such as hospitals, hotels, service camps, approved schools, etc.), although the figures for this latter category apply to 1951 only and the corresponding 1931 figures had to be obtained from the relevant volume of the Census of that date.

ASPECTS TO BE CONSIDERED

Unlike the previous example only one major aspect of the figures will be treated. The aim is to produce a map which will establish a picture of differential aspects of population change throughout the area and for this purpose *the change must be expressed relatively, e.g. as a percentage increase or decrease, rather than numerically*. Because of their very different nature and fortunes during the period under study *it would be desirable for the map to differentiate clearly between urban and rural areas.*

GENERAL STATISTICAL CONSIDERATIONS

The hard core of the problem here has already been touched upon in Chapter 3. The published figures, which relate to the component Rural Districts as a whole have already been shown frequently to be meaningless, the administrative boundary lines often arbitrarily containing areas of very different types so far as their recent population history is concerned. Unfortunately, breaking down the figures into individual parishes, which seems at first sight the most likely way of overcoming this difficulty, would not be a particularly satisfactory solution for it was also pointed out in Chapter 3 that the majority of the parishes within this county are so small in total population that random variations could easily produce figures just as arbitrary as those for whole Rural Districts. Even if this had not been the case the result of dealing with individual parishes would have been a map so patchy and fussy that it would have been impossible to deduce from it the dominant trends suggested by the mass of detailed information. The only solution, therefore, is to seek some grouping of parishes more logical than the administrative one, large enough in total population and uniform enough in aspects of change to allow a reasonably representative figure to be given for it.

To do this the individual figures for the change in all parishes were first calculated and plotted on tracing paper placed over a map indicating parish boundaries. Examination of the 'run' of the figures on this map facilitated the grouping of parishes showing reasonably similar trends, and a figure for the change for the whole group was obtained by calculating the total population of the component parishes, in 1931 and 1951. Urban areas, including any necessary adjoining parishes, were always treated separately, as was any place with a population of over 800. This last figure was established from a dispersal graph of parish population size and was chosen because it represented a type of big village, quite unlike the normal village in the area, and moreover seemed large enough at least to allow cancelling out of most of the random errors.

For the rural areas the method worked quite well. To avoid leaving the odd small parish on its own, exceptions to the general group-trend had sometimes to be included, but in only a very few cases did the figures for individual parishes differ by more than 4% from the group figure; and the total population of the group rarely fell below 800 (it was often two or three times this figure) so that once again the effect of random variations would be considerably removed. Another important feature in obtaining representative and comparable values throughout the areas was the decision to use the figure relating to *population in private households* and *not* total population as the basis for the calculation of change, at least for all rural groups and towns with below about 10,000 population. In towns larger than this the changes calculated from either set of figures never differed by any significant amount and in many cases with these larger towns boundary changes made it impossible to obtain comparable figures for the population in private households in 1931 and 1951. For smaller towns and especially for some rural parishes the two figures differed very much indeed, perhaps the most notable case of all being the small town of Leyburn where the two results were as follows:

Fig. 41. Population Change in the North Riding of Yorkshire, 1931-51.
Source: Registrar-General, *Census of England and Wales*, 1931 and 1951. County Volume. Yorkshire (East an̄
North Ridings); London (H.M.S.O.), 1954.

Key to towns shown. BC Barnard Castle-Startforth: BE Bedale-Aiskew: E Easingwold: G Guisborough: H Helmsley: HA Hawes: K Kirkby Moorside: L Loftus: LE Leyburn: M Middlesbrough: MN Malton-Norton: N Northallerton-Romanby: P Pickering: R Richmond: RE Redcar: S Skelton: SM Saltburn-Marske: ST Stokesley: T Thornaby: TK Thirsk-Sowerby: Y Yarm.

	1931	*1951*	*Change*	*Change* %
Total population	1,440	1,281	−159	−11%
Population in private households	728	1,202	474	65%

The remarkable difference being solely due to the presence of a temporary military camp in Leyburn on census night in 1931. It is the presence of particularly large numbers of service-men on aerodromes and Army camps which is responsible for *some* of the worst anomalies in the figures for whole Rural Districts given in Chapter 3, but examination of detailed figures for individual parishes shows that less obvious 'institutional' factors are responsible for misleading results being obtained from the total population figures in a considerable number of cases. To obtain a figure which purports to represent change in a parish but which in fact reflects not conditions generally but merely the fact that four more old people now reside in a home for the aged, and then to use that figure to make comparison with conditions in neighbouring areas is surely a pointless task. Comparison needs a figure based on relatively uniform conditions and one derived from the 'private households' total will provide this.

CHOICE OF METHOD AND DETAILS

The modified statistics prepared as described above related to a series of areas of varying size and, as in the previous example, there was no difficulty in choosing a satisfactory method; some form of shading technique was a natural choice. The main secondary consideration here was a statistical one. The representative figures for each area had been obtained only as a result of considerable calculation and it seemed pointless to allow this work to be lost again in the broad shading-groupings of the normal shading map, so that some means of retaining accurate representation of the value was desirable. As a first choice proportional shading, as in Fig. 17F (p. 53) was envisaged, but lack of colour proved a serious disadvantage. With two colours, one for increase and one for decrease, and by slightly modifying the method so that the colours became solid at only moderately large values (everything above that value being shown in solid colour representing an unusually large increase or decrease) a reasonable vertical scale for the shaded bands would have been obtained and the method might have worked well. Unfortunately this technique was impracticable in black and white. The idea of replacing the two colours by two tones, e.g. solid for increase and dotted for decrease, seemed unlikely to differentiate satisfactorily between positive and negative changes and to use one tone only, so that the range of values had to include both negative and positive ones, would have given too restricted a vertical scale. Instead, recourse was had to a normal type of shading map with shading-groups established from a dispersal graph, but with the actual value superimposed wherever space permitted this.

Differentiation between urban and rural areas was achieved by using a uniform circular symbol for all urban areas (whether administratively Urban Districts or not) though in all other cases area limits were taken from actual parish boundaries. Urban areas are thus quite easily recognised on the map and the scatter of circular symbols (which are named) provides a useful framework to help the map user locate the various subdivisions of the rural areas. To assist this latter process even further within the rural areas themselves, the main water-sheds are marked unobtrusively, enabling the Pennine Dales or Eskdale west of Whitby, for example, to be located easily without the need for adding more names to the map.

GENERAL CONCLUSIONS DERIVED FROM FIG. 41

The map emphasises above all things the detailed complexity of population change in this area and destroys absolutely the idea of facile approximations based on figures for entire Rural Districts. In particular, certain important areas of depopulation stand out, notably the centre of the Vale of Pickering and the remote valleys enclosed by moorland in both the Pennines and the North York Moors, although even in these cases conditions are far from uniform over large areas. Other factors which emerge are the unusually complicated pattern of change in the northern portion of the Vale of York, and, outside that area a tendency for the noticeable increases in population to be confined to urban areas and to the quite restricted areas of 'suburban expansion' around York, Scarborough and Tees-side. In the case of the three last mentioned areas the *numbers* involved are quite large and are particularly apt grossly to distort the figures for much wider areas if returns are made for entire Rural Districts.

EXAMPLE 3. ASSESSING THE EFFECT OF THE INTERACTION OF TWO RELATED COMPONENTS WITHIN THE DISTRIBUTION OF ONE MAIN VARIABLE. ANALYSIS OF THE POPULATION CHANGE WITHIN THE CENTRAL PORTION OF THE WEST RIDING OF YORK- SHIRE, 1931-1951 (FIGS. 42-45)

In the previous example population change was considered quite simply as a single variable. The figure given was that of total change and no attempt was made to investigate any factors which contributed towards that figure. In practice it is well known that this population change is the result of the interaction of two factors, natural increase and migration, and that quite similar total changes in two areas may result from the interaction of these factors in very dissimilar fashion. Natural increase is the population change which would result in any area from the excess of births over deaths (in some areas in Britain excess of deaths over births is occasionally encountered), and this figure in any area and for any intercensal period can be calculated from the returns of births and deaths made to the Registrar-General. The term migration is self-explanatory, but somewhat misleading. What is implied is *net* migration, i.e. excess of immigrants over emigrants or vice versa in any particular area, and this figure is usually obtained as the difference between the total change and natural increase thus:

	Natural Increase	Total Change	Assumed Net Migration
Area A	6·0%	16·0%	10·0%
Area B	17·0%	9·0%	−8·0%

The task which is being attempted is a study of population change within an area not simply in terms of total change but also by analysis into these two component parts, with areas classified differentially on this basis.

SOURCE AND STATISTICAL CONSIDERATIONS

Information on all three aspects, total change, natural increase and migration for the period 1931-51 is available, for each administrative area, in the West Riding volume of the 1951 Census of England and Wales. For urban areas this can be considered relatively

Fig. 42. Components of Population Change in Part of the West Riding of Yorkshire 1931-51. *Fig. 42A.* Changes due to natural increase. *Fig. 42B.* Changes due to migration. *Source:* Registrar-General, *Census of England and Wales, 1951*, County Volume, Yorkshire (West Riding); London (H.M.S.O.), 1954.

Fig. 43. Population Change in Part of the West Riding of Yorkshire, 1931-51.
Fig. 43A. By simple shading technique without consideration of components.
Fig. 43B. By shading technique adapted to show dominant components as well.

Source: As Fig. 42.

satisfactory, but for rural areas, where only composite figures are available for each Rural District, serious misgivings arise. It is disconcerting to find, for example, a figure of $+17\cdot0\%$ given for migration for the whole of Wharfedale R.D. within which individual parishes show frequent *total* changes of -10% to -20% or more with implications of possible *negative* migrational changes in excess of these figures. Unfortunately, figures for natural increase and migration are not available for individual parishes and since it is obvious that, as in the last example, figures for entire Rural Districts lump together individual parishes of greatly dissimilar type some attempt at a breakdown of the published figures is essential.

It is not easy accurately to provide this breakdown, but an approximation which is at least superior to the unadjusted values can be obtained starting from the total change which occurred in *groups of parishes* after the manner described in the previous example. Once this total change is established, if the same figure for natural increase is used as for the whole Rural District, a new figure for the net migration from each group of parishes can be obtained as indicated above. The validity of the results is dependent on the reliability of the assumption that the figure for natural increase remains relatively constant throughout a whole Rural District. Fortunately, the figures for natural increase, when plotted separately as in Fig. 42A, do show a fairly gradual and even trend throughout much of the map, so that rapid variations within a small area are unlikely. Fig. 42A also suggests the possibility of calculating intermediate values, but the fact that within each group of parishes two or three intermediate values might have to be used would lead to excessively complicated calculations; and as this would still not entirely remove the element of approximation, it was decided generally to adopt a uniform natural increase figure for the whole Rural District. An exception to this rule was made in the case of Doncaster, Hemsworth and Osgoldcross Rural Districts which occupy much of the area between Doncaster, Barnsley and Pontefract. The trend of values in Fig. 42A suggests that the remarkable gradual increase towards the south-west corner of the map is in some way related to the increasing importance of coal mining within the area and in each of these three Rural Districts mining areas are intermixed with enclaves more noticeably in agricultural use. Accordingly, for the agricultural areas in these districts a figure for natural increase roughly comparable with that in adjoining agricultural Rural Districts was assumed, and from this the resultant natural increase for the rest of the Rural District could be calculated.

As an example of the discrepancy between published figures for the whole Rural District and the figures actually used, the detailed breakdown is given below for that portion of Wharfedale R.D. contained within the map. Though the figures are necessarily only *estimates* it cannot be doubted that they are to be preferred to the highly unrepresentative figure for the whole Rural District.

	Total Change	Natural Increase	Assumed Migration
Wharfedale R.D. (whole)	$25\cdot2\%$	$8\cdot2\%$	$17\cdot0\%$
(1) Parishes north-west of Otley	$-16\cdot8\%$	$8\cdot2\%$	$-25\cdot0\%$
(2) Newall-with-Clifton, adjacent to Otley	$9\cdot6\%$	$8\cdot2\%$	$1\cdot4\%$
(3) Parishes north-east of Otley	$-2\cdot3\%$	$8\cdot2\%$	$-10\cdot5\%$
(4) Parishes between Otley and Leeds	$50\cdot4\%$	$8\cdot2\%$	$42\cdot2\%$

No modifications were made to any other figures except in the case of Doncaster County Borough whose anomalous boundary was 'redrawn' to include the Urban District of Bentley-with-Arksey and the parish of Sprotborough, Doncaster's obvious suburbs lying north of the River Don.

CHOICE OF METHOD AND DETAILS

The problem to be solved here is the most involved which has been considered so far, and it is not surprising that it offers at least two possible lines of approach. The first of these is what might be termed the 'obvious' or simple one and consists in presenting the final picture through *three* maps, one to show the overall change and establish the basic pattern under investigation, and two more, one each to illustrate natural increase and migrational change. The last two maps would provide further illustrations of trends and background information with which to reassess the implications of the first map.

If this approach is used, the cartographic problems involved are relatively simple, but the ultimate aim of the study is really achieved not cartographically but *mentally*, being left to the perception of the map user. The second line of approach which presents much more serious cartographic problems, requires some technique which shall contain *on one map* a representation of both change *and* its component elements. Let us examine each of these approaches in turn.

The three maps needed for the first approach do not present any serious difficulties other than the need for better statistical information regarding rural areas already mentioned. In each case the figures used relate to areas and for the map of *total* change a well-designed shading map (Fig. 43A) seems most likely to fulfil the requirements of telling as straightforward and specific a story as possible, indicating the various areas used, their location and the amount of total change. Originally it was hoped to include additionally within each area, in figures, the actual amount of change, but within the limitations of black and white technique this proved impossible; each value would have had to be placed in a 'window' which would in turn have given rise to difficulties in naming sufficient areas to provide the index of location which was just as necessary as a representation of values. With colour techniques the possibility of over-printing names and figures on differently coloured shading would have made it possible to incorporate these desirable additions quite easily. As a substitute for this absolute precision a fairly large number of shading tones (9) was used and each of these was designed to cover as narrow a range of values as possible, the actual limits being determined in the usual way from a dispersal graph.

An alternative, precise solution would have been some form of proportional shading, but on the whole the range of values was too wide and more particularly many of the areas were too small to make this method very feasible. As in the previous example, the lack of colour differentiation between positive and negative values had to be overcome by using increasing intensity of shading, the very lowest values being left blank and the position of zero being emphasised by a change from dot to line shading close to that value (actually at $+1 \cdot 2\%$).

The two supplementary maps serve rather different needs and demand slightly different treatment. Unlike the first map, which had to be as definite as possible, these would be more suitably designed to show *trends* within the area so that their message could be fairly quickly assimilated by the map user and mentally stored for use in assessing the first map. Of course it would be perfectly feasible to present the information here by exactly the same technique as was used for Fig. 43A, but it was felt that this would only overwhelm the map user with more detail than he could comfortably handle and that a combination of one fairly precise and two fairly generalised maps was much more manageable. For the illustration of trends among a series of plotted values relating to areas, the isoline map is an obvious choice and this technique has been used for both maps. The first map (Fig. 42A), relating to natural increase, presented no problems and the isolines have been drawn by interpolation as described in Chapter 2, plus a certain amount of guidance from the run of the local authority boundaries. The figures for migration were not so easily dismissed, however. Unlike natural increase, trends were not always gradual and in particular awkward 'islands' of quite considerable increase were often found amidst much lower or even decreasing values. To have introduced these in the normal way would have involved tedious building up to the required value by numerous closely spaced ring isolines; this seemed both messy and unnecessary and it was decided to treat these instances as anomalies in the general pattern by breaking the normal run of the isolines and simply inserting a high value 'blob' across them, much in the same way that isolated unconformities are marked on a geological map. The method is both neat and clear and much to be preferred to the tedious orthodox approach to such high values.

The cartographic rendering of the techniques presented few particular problems, so long as the maps needed only to be used to express trends and the same 'reference framework' of places was used as in Fig. 43. Lack of different colours for negative and positive values was again a handicap and unfortunately with rather dissimilar ranges (the natural increase figures are almost all positive but the migration figures are balanced fairly evenly about zero) it did not prove entirely practicable to maintain comparable shading types for roughly similar values on both maps, shading as opposed to dot stipples beginning at $+9 \cdot 5$ on the natural increase map but at $-7 \cdot 5$ on the migration one; had two colours been available a greater variety of shading would have been possible and this small objection would have been quite easily overcome.

So much for the first approach. Let us leave an assessment of the results until those of the second method, with its more intricate cartographic problems, are available for comparison. The main problem involved in the second approach is to come to a sufficient understanding of the figures before we begin the cartography. A thorough analysis of both totals and components is needed and fortunately we have already encountered, in the scatter graph, a simple statistical technique which can be used to analyse the different ways in which two components occur together. So far the scatter graph has only been considered as a means of considering relationships between two components which were rather separate entities (e.g. houses and people), but in this case the two components not only both refer to the same thing (people) but are expressed in a uniform fashion, using values which are capable of being added or subtracted from one another to produce an end product which is also under investigation. This peculiar combination of circumstances enables much more information to be obtained from the scatter graph than is normally the case and a little 'thinking aloud' about what happens on the graph in this case will help understanding of the distribution and analysis of the final figures.

Fig. 44 illustrates some of this thinking aloud. Consider, for example, what happens if we plot on the graph a series of points whose individual figures are as follows (natural increase first and all values in percentages):

A −5, 5; B 10, −10; C 20, −20; D −5, 10; E 10, −5; F 20, −15; G −5, 0; H 5, −10; J 15, −20

The nine points consist, in effect, of three sets of three, with total changes of 0, 5 and −5 respectively and it will be seen that each set lies along a straight line at an angle of 45° to each axis. A little thought will show that any number of similar diagonal lines could be drawn on the graph and that all points along any one such line would have the *same total change*, irrespective of the size of the components; conversely, we can use lines like these to divide up the scatter of points on the graph and produce groups which have total changes above or below the particular value selected. It is not difficult to draw in the line representing any particular total change. All that is needed is to devise two pairs of components which will produce this required change, plot them on the graph and join the plotted points by a straight line.

Thinking about the graph in this way soon enables one to appreciate further significant ideas, such as the implication of a point being situated in different parts of the graph. The line ABC for example divides the graph into two parts, with total change positive above that line and negative below it. Similarly, along certain lines specific things can be said to happen. Along XX, YY and ZZ, for example, one factor is always zero, the other factor therefore being entirely responsible for any change, and from this it is an easy step to realising that for points *close* to these lines one factor will be very small, probably negligible. We can also find other lines such as PP where both factors are equal, but are accentuating one another because both are positive, or a line like QQ where one factor is twice the other. From lines such as these it is not difficult to label the intervening areas of the graph as having certain characteristics which will help to subdivide sensibly the scatter of plotted values when these have to be studied.

The actual scatter graph used in the analysis of the figures is reproduced in Fig. 45. At first sight the points appear to lie awkwardly widespread, but a second glance shows that there is perhaps a crude tendency for many of them to lie along a broad diagonal band astride the position of the 'no change' line (see Fig. 44)—in other words in many of the areas total changes are small, chiefly because negative migration is counteracting positive natural increase. This is a useful beginning to a classification of the results and it would seem sensible to try to introduce into it some idea of the amount of total change. A straightforward *dispersal* graph was made for the total change figures and indicated that values of plus and minus 1·2% and plus and minus 6% would act as suitable demarcating points, and lines for these amounts of total change were therefore plotted on the scatter graph. Unfortunately, the three categories so defined contain places of similar total change, but very differently sized components, some being due to the interaction of values of less than 1% whilst others have values both more than 20%. Each of the three basic divisions was, therefore, further subdivided into three according to the *size of the components*, simply by drawing horizontal and vertical lines across the bands. So that a reasonably concise 'label' could be added to each group it was desirable

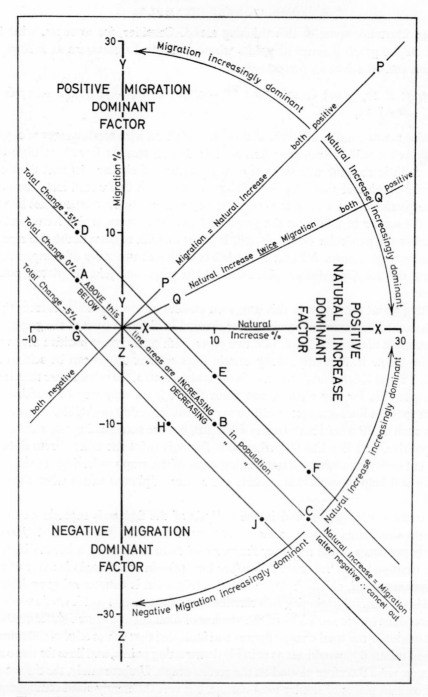

Fig. 44. A 'Sketch' Scatter Graph to illustrate the components in Fig. 42, showing significance of situation on certain lines or in certain areas of the graph.

Fig. 45. Actual Scatter Graph of the Values used in constructing Figs. 42 and
43. *Source:* As Fig. 42.

that the limits for both migration and natural increase should have the same values, and in this case the limits of $\pm 7 \cdot 5\%$ and $\pm 15\%$ divided each band conveniently into three sections. With these limits only four points fall in the stippled areas on Fig. 45; they comply with one but not the other limiting value, but these are treated as anomalies and included in the most suitable adjacent group.

About half the plotted points in Fig. 45 fell within the classification so far devised and the remaining values fortunately presented rather clear characteristics, corresponding roughly to three groups situated in parts of the graph which indicated that migration, natural increase and negative migration were dominant factors respectively, and a fourth group in which the most unusual feature, if not the largest, was a *negative* natural increase. Each of these four groups could be further subdivided according to whether total changes involved were in excess of 16% and 25% if positive and $-12\cdot 5\%$ if negative, all of these additional limiting values being suggested by a dispersal graph of total change for all plotted points. The total effect produced by all the various limits imposed on Fig. 45 was to divide the results into eight groups, based on amount of total change, subdivided in each case into two or three categories according to the dominant factors or nature of the main components.

The representation of this twofold classification presented something of a notational problem which was solved by devising eight basic types of shading for total change, supplemented by letters to indicate the componental aspects. 'O' in three sizes was invoked to show those cases where figures tended to cancel each other out and 'M' or 'N' to indicate areas where migration or natural increase were dominant; no sign was attached to the 'M' or 'N' as this was presupposed from the negative or positive nature of the basic shading.

The application of this technique is illustrated in Fig. 43B (p. 123) and the result is not unlike Fig. 43A in many respects. This is hardly surprising, for the technique, a straightforward shading map, is basically the same, but in this case the usefulness of the specific information on *amount* of change is enormously increased by the additional information concerning its *nature* or more especially its dominant component. There are also certain detailed points of difference between the two maps; only eight types of shading have been used in Fig. 43B to fit in better with the more complex considerations of the dual notation and from this point of view the necessity of carrying two aspects of change has produced a slightly less specific map. Unlike the previous example negative and positive values have been differentiated by different types of shading (dots and lines respectively) with the blanks being retained for values around zero. These near-zero values almost always coincided with areas where components were cancelling one another out and the blank space seemed particularly symbolic of this 'not much-happening-in-the-end' state of affairs.

COMPARATIVE ASSESSMENT OF RESULTS AND CONCLUSIONS

Through the medium of Figs. 42 and 43 the relative merits of the two approaches to this particular problem can now be compared. If the first or orthodox line of approach is taken it cannot be doubted that Fig. 43A gives a clear picture of total change and allows an easy appreciation of the main points regarding this. In the left-hand portion of the map outside the larger, named towns total change is usually either small or slightly negative, although the named towns themselves generally show rather larger positive changes, and a well-defined area of marked increase occurs around or adjacent to many of them, especially Leeds and Bradford. In the western corner of the map towards Todmorden, in an area of very marked relief, quite large negative total changes occur.

In contrast to this relatively simple picture the right-hand half of the map exhibits much more complicated patterns. The southern area around Barnsley and Rotherham is one of general increase, often quite large in amount though very patchy in detail, and with suggestions of the same broken rings of greater increase around towns such as Rotherham as occurred around the towns in the west. The eastern corner of this section of the map, however, is generally an area of marked decrease with the obvious exceptions of a belt east of and including Pontefract and a 'pepper-pot' distribution of isolated high values which is typical of the whole of this right-hand portion of the map.

Despite these easily drawn conclusions it must be remembered that a simple realisation of the amount of total change is not the main object of this particular exercise and the question which must now be answered is how far we can effectively appreciate the differing backgrounds of these types of total change by a perusal of Figs. 42A and B. Fortunately, the patterns indicated on Fig. 42A are simple and relatively easily committed to memory, being composed simply of a steadily increasing trend in a clockwise direction from large negative values in the western corner to a maximum along a line almost due east from Barnsley; a trough of rather lower values occurs between that town, Rotherham and Sheffield, but there is renewed increase east of Rotherham again. Fig. 42B is another matter, however. Unlike natural increase, migration shows a less rational pattern and many of the complications of Fig. 43A appear to have their roots in the intricate patterns found on Fig. 42B. As in Fig. 42A the left-hand portion of the map is relatively simple with areas of marked 'suburban increase' around and between Leeds, Bradford and Halifax, but in the right-hand portion the extremely complicated patterns almost defy general description apart from the Pontefract 'ridge' and the area of marked decrease around Doncaster.

The unfortunate coincidence of the most intricate portion of Fig. 42B with the only portion of Fig. 42A where patterns become at all complicated, points to the inevitable conclusion that only a person remarkably well blessed with visual perception and awareness will be able to supplement Fig. 43A with anything other than the most vague and general observations compounded from Fig. 42.

By comparison with this hit-or-miss method the much more elaborate Fig. 43B, which illustrates the second approach, seems to guarantee more positive results. Admittedly, Fig. 43B is more complicated than Fig. 43A, so that it is a map to be inspected and sampled rather than glanced at, but inspection will produce clearly and incontrovertibly the answer which is being sought. It is now possible, for example, to differentiate easily between the discontinuous 'rings' around Leeds and Bradford where migration is dominant and that around Barnsley where the retention of a high rate of natural increase is playing a much larger part. Contrast too the areas north of Otley and around Todmorden; both show considerable decreases, but in one emigration, in the other negative natural increase is the main cause. In like fashion the area of small change or light decrease which runs horizontally across the middle portion of the map is generally produced by opposing, cancelling factors of small magnitude around Bradford and Halifax, but of much greater size between Wakefield and Barnsley.

Such a comparison of the effectiveness of the two approaches points to a conclusion which needs no further underlining. The practice, still commonly encountered in articles, books and national atlases, of presenting related information in the form of a series of maps in the hope that these can be assimilated in compound manner by the map user falls far short of what is really required. The responsibility of the process of fusion lies with the cartographer not the observer, and demands more subtle and sophisticated approaches if it is to be successful. The *apparent* complexity of the end-products of this second approach, disconcerting though it may appear at first glance, is much to be preferred to the inefficient and misleading simplicity of more orthodox solutions.

EXAMPLE 4. A DISTRIBUTION CONCERNED WITH MULTIPLE VARIABLES. AGRICULTURAL LAND USE IN SWEDEN, 1959 (FIGS. 46 AND 47).

The examples so far described have all been concerned with situations in which no more than one or two variable factors had to be considered. Not infrequently, however, distributions with multiple variables occur and have to be portrayed visually, the most commonly encountered examples of this type of distribution being found in statistics relating to land use or employment. In these cases the complete entity of total land used or numbers employed is presented as being divided up into several categories of different land use or types of industry, the proportions of these varying at each place for which figures are given. As an example of problems involving this type of distribution, an attempt is made here to illustrate the variations in agricultural land use throughout Sweden in 1959.

SOURCE AND ASPECTS TO BE CONSIDERED

The basic source of the figures used in this particular problem is Table 60 of the *Statistical Yearbook of Sweden* for 1960. In that table the total acreage of land in agricultural use is given for each of the twenty-four counties of Sweden and this total is further subdivided into land under seventeen major crops or uses, whilst Table 46 in the same source enables this agricultural area to be seen against the total area of other land uses (forest, unused land, built-up areas, etc.) in each county. The aim of this study is to illustrate this changing pattern of land use by means of a map which will produce a *fusion of impressions* illustrating not merely land use but the varying pattern of agriculture in Sweden, distinguishing changes in emphasis from one part of the country to another and picking out the marked similarities which occur between region and region no less than their differences.

GENERAL STATISTICAL CONSIDERATIONS

Any comparative study of figures relating to different administrative areas demands statistics presented in comparable form and the first major task here is to translate the values for the actual number of hectares in the seventeen use classes in each of the twenty-four counties into percentages of total land in agricultural use. At this point, however, anticipation of the later stages of the work suggests that some of the 408 calculations involved might be superfluous, for the simple fact is that *we cannot deal with seventeen variables*. Admittedly, two methods described in Chapter 2 (divided circles and divided rectangles) were adapted to illustrate variable components and could certainly accommodate seventeen sectors or slices, but the main problem here is mental and visual rather than mechanical. If we had misgivings about the simple comparisons involved in the previous example it will be readily apparent that we shall not get far with a visual assessment of the changes in twenty-four examples with seventeen variables in each. *The first requirement, therefore, is to reduce the number of variables to more manageable proportions.* In effect this has been achieved by reducing their number to *three* and several advantages accrue from such a drastic telescoping of the detailed picture. In the first place we have already encountered a device, the triangular graph, which will enable us to plot entities composed of three (but no more) components and allow the easy recognition of similar and dissimilar occurrences, so that there is a strong, statistical reason for choosing such a number. Fortunately, agricultural considerations do not run counter to this. Despite its many detailed variations, Swedish agriculture (the same is true of many countries) can be viewed as a dual activity—namely, the raising of livestock with all this implies and the growing of crops for other purposes, either for human consumption locally or for sale. So far as the livestock sector of the economy is concerned there is in Sweden a dual basis of grass or hay from either permanent or rotation grassland, and the growing of crops for animal feeding-stuffs so that a threefold division into grass and hay (grass), crops grown for animal feeding-stuffs (animal crops) and crops grown mainly for human consumption or sale (cash and other crops) will effectively delineate the main preoccupations of the Swedish farmer. This division is not entirely rigid of course. Some crops such as hay, fodder beet and sugar beet fall clearly into one of the main categories, but others such as barley or potatoes could find a place in two. Where this occurs these crops have been consistently included in that division which accounts for the bulk of the acreage—thus barley is always considered as an 'animal crop', potatoes as a 'cash crop' because this is predominantly the case throughout most of Sweden.

With such a threefold division it now appears necessary only to calculate the total in each of the *groups*[1] as a percentage of the whole and many detailed calculations have been eliminated. Of necessity the figures for 'fallow and unused arable land' have had to be eliminated from the total; they could not be allotted to any of the major groups and to have introduced a fourth sector would have destroyed the whole basis of the subsequent analysis. Since land in this category usually occupied between 3% and 7% of the total agricultural land the omission, though awkward, is not serious.

CHOICE OF METHODS AND DETAILS

Having reduced our original figures to manageable proportions, we are now in a position to elucidate the broad patterns which these suggest by plotting the percentage figures for each of the three main sectors in each county on a triangular graph as in Fig. 46. The results there indicate that despite their variety the figures for the twenty-four counties can be simplified into five groups with varying degrees of precision. Some groups, e.g. groups 4 and 5 are clearly defined, others, e.g. groups 2 and 3, much less obviously so, and group 1 which contains the solitary county of Malmohus emphasises the unique position of that remarkable

[1] For the crops included in each group see the key in Fig. 47 (p. 135).

county in Swedish agriculture. Only one county, Kalmar, lies awkwardly outside any of these five groupings and since it is by no means as important and unique as Malmohus it has had to be included anomalously with group 3A with which it shows most similarities. Each of the five main groupings can be fairly satisfactorily defined by means of average values for each of the three component sectors and the results can be differentiated on a map by means of a simple shading technique.

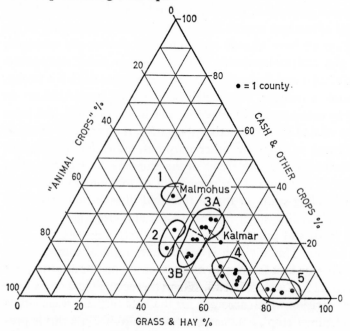

Fig. 46. A Triangular Graph to show Allocation of Agricultural Land in the counties of Sweden among three constituent uses. *Source:* Statistiska Centralbyran, *Statistisk Arsbok för Sverige, 1960,* Stockholm, 1960.

As Fig. 47 shows, this is a most useful preliminary as the juxtaposition of the counties within each group does in fact divide Sweden up into some half-dozen or so more or less continuous areas, each with a characteristic basic agricultural pattern to which the detailed information can now be added.

Although seventeen initial variables have been reduced to three it was never intended that the original seventeen should disappear completely from the picture. Some form of representation of the distribution of the more important of these crops is just as necessary as representation of the overall pattern, but it is essential that this latter feature should be established first so that the detail is seen against an appreciable background and not simply as profusion of isolated occurrences.

Fortunately, the use of a shading technique for the first, general considerations will permit the inclusion of another 'single-symbol' technique superimposed on the shading, and for this purpose the threefold subdivision was represented by means of a pie graph for each county. Each of these pie-graph symbols enables the actual variations in the component parts to be shown and also acts as a base against which detailed information concerning specific crops can be placed. As with earlier considerations, the temptation to add a profusion of detail must be avoided and it was, therefore, decided to indicate only the really important crops which contributed to each sector, these being easily added by placing a series of letters against the relevant section of the pie graph. Crops considered sufficiently important to warrant particular mention were those which occupied 50% or more, or 33% to 50% of the land *within their particular sector.* In the case of some cash and other crops where the greater variety possible meant that such figures were rarely encountered the figure of

Fig. 47. Agricultural Land Use in Sweden, 1959. *Source:* As Fig. 46.

135

more than 20% was substituted as a lower limit (see Fig. 47). The use of such simple figures for subdivision meant that the need to include or exclude any crop from the notation could almost always be determined by observation without calculation, and the decision to base the percentages on land *within a particular sector* and not on percentages of *total* land meant that changing regional emphasis within the broad framework already defined would be well illustrated.

Further points of detail are the confining of the background shading in the northern provinces only to those areas where agriculture assumed any importance, and the addition of an inset map showing the percentage of total land in agricultural use, to indicate how widespread or otherwise were the conditions represented on the main map.

GENERAL CONCLUSIONS DERIVED FROM FIG. 47

Fig. 47 emphasises once again the success of this compound method over the more orthodox approach of multiple-sectored unannotated pie graphs so often used for this type of statistics. Not only are valid basic patterns of Swedish agriculture established from out of a mass of detail but similarities in detail are also emphasised and the distribution of individual crops and transitional tendencies in the crops grown in each sector are well illustrated. Consider, for example, the way in which the map brings out the transitional tendencies in the animal crop sector from the extreme dominance of the very tolerant six-rowed barley (B) in the north, through a gradually increasing acreage of oats (b.o.) in Gavleborgs and Kopparberg, to the extreme dominance of oats (O) further south and the re-emergence of barley (this time of the two-rowed variety) in the extreme south and in Gotland. Regional specialisations such as potatoes (P) or (p) on the sandy soils of the south-east, or oil-seeds (x) in the eastern counties emerge quite clearly, whilst consistent regional associations in all sectors, e.g. BPH in the north, WHO, WpHO and Wxhm in Central Sweden are all apparent.

CHAPTER SEVEN

Sources of Statistics

IN a work of this kind, where space is limited, it is always difficult to decide whether to include some description of sources of statistical information. The tremendous bulk and diversity of even the most obvious statistical sources has already prompted entire books devoted to this topic alone, so that any attempt to condense information into no more than one chapter seems scarcely worth making; yet even so two basic problems remain. The complete novice seeking statistical information for the first time needs guidance, even of the broadest possible sort, before he can get started at all; whilst the more experienced worker still finds unexpected difficulties which the elaborate existing reference works will not entirely help him to overcome quickly.

It is with the main aim of solving these two particular problems that this chapter is designed, and its arrangement follows from them. A very brief guide to the principal sources of statistics of an international kind is followed by a second section which is confined to describing sources of British statistics, also in outline form except in those sections which the author has found to present most difficulties in practice. This latter section in particular makes no pretence to completeness, and reference should also be made to the detailed works listed in the text.

One further general aspect remains to be mentioned. For the successful *mapping* of statistics *two* aspects must normally be considered—namely, 'How much or how many?' and 'Where?' Unfortunately, the same source does not often answer both questions and what may be described as 'quantitative' and 'locational' sources will usually be described separately and in that order.

SOURCES OF STATISTICS OF A NATIONAL AND INTERNATIONAL NATURE

Perhaps the most easily accessible source of statistical information on the various countries of the world (though not generally world totals) is the *Statesman's Yearbook*, published annually in London. A typical volume provides, for each country, a 'hard core' of statistics on subjects such as area, population, administration, social services, industrial and agricultural production, imports and exports, and provides in many cases comparable figures for the preceding few years.

Similar but much fuller information, together with world totals, appears in the *Statistical Yearbook* published by the United Nations. The main headings under which information is provided are population, manpower, production (of all kinds), construction, energy, consumption, transport, communication, trade, balance of payments, international economic aid, wages and prices, national income, finance, housing, social statistics and education. Since 1959 most tables show figures for 1948 and the nine years previous to publication, but volumes for 1958 and earlier also include some pre-war years. A sister-volume, the *Demographic Yearbook*, adds more detailed information on population, births, deaths and marriages, and the *Monthly Bulletin of Statistics* also published by the United Nations provides figures on more specialised selected topics.

Another shorter source of world statistics is J. C. Weaver and F. E. Lukerman, *World Resource Statistics* (2nd Edition), Minneapolis, 1955. Topics covered include population, power, minerals, forestry, fisheries, agriculture and industry, usually with three or more comparable figures for past years, including pre-war ones. Statistics relating to the U.S.A. are rather more detailed than others and a useful feature is the expression of most totals as a percentage of world production as well as quantitatively.

For climatic statistics, which are usually missing from the works already referred to, two excellent sources are available. For many years now students have abstracted figures from W. G. Kendrew, *Climates of the Continents* (4th Edition), Oxford, 1953, and this has recently been supplemented by the *Tables of Temperature, Relative Humidity, and Precipitation for the World* prepared by the Meteorological Office and published in six parts by H.M.S.O., London, 1958.

Naturally, only a minimum of information about any country can be provided in a volume covering the whole world and for greater detail one must turn to works covering individual countries. Many states now publish a national yearbook, either descriptive with some statistics or, in many cases, entirely statistical in its nature. Examples of the latter type, taken mainly from Western Europe are *Annual Abstract of Statistics*, Central Statistical Office, published by H.M.S.O., London;[1] *Annuaire Statistique de la France*, Institut National de la Statistique et des Études Économiques, Paris; *Statistisches Jahrbuch für die Bundesrepublik Deutschland*, Statistisches Bundesamt, Wiesbaden; *Statistisches Jahrbuch der Deutschen Demokratischen Republik*, Staatliche Zentralverwaltung für Statistik, Berlin, and *Statistical Abstract of the United States*, Bureau of the Census, Washington, D.C.[2]

Though differing in detail, these yearbooks have much in common, showing similarity of information, both among themselves and with the international sources just described. Thus the British 'Annual Abstract' has sections on Area and Climate, Population and Vital Statistics, Social Conditions, Education, Labour, Production, Distribution, Transport, External Trade, Finance, National Income and Expenditure, Banking and Insurance, and Prices. In these respects it resembles those of other countries, although in detail it is poorer on agriculture and land use, external trade by particular countries and cargoes handled at individual ports; detailed statistics for all of these are published elsewhere (see below).

[1] This can be supplemented by (1) a *Monthly Digest of Statistics*, (2) from 1953, a separate *Digest of Scottish Statistics*, (3) from 1954, a separate *Digest of Welsh Statistics*. The Scottish volume is published twice yearly by the Statistical Office, Edinburgh, the rest by H.M.S.O., London, who also publish a *Digest of Colonial Statistics* for the Colonial Office.

[2] Another very useful condensed source referring to the United States is the *County and City Data Book, 1956*, also published by the Bureau of the Census.

Pertinent to the mapping of statistics is the fact that most yearbooks attempt some territorial breakdown of national totals, usually into those units forming the next tier in the administrative hierarchy (statistics for individual places are practically never given except for population, and trade at specific ports) producing figures for areas of greatly differing size, some conveniently small, others so large that wide variations can still occur within their boundaries. The following table illustrates these contrasts. It is greatly to be regretted that the British sources attempt no greater breakdown than by *countries*, for there is no information at county level in the 'Annual Abstract'.

Country	Area 1,000's Sq. Miles	Administrative Subdivision	No.	Average Area 1,000's Sq. Miles
United Kingdom	94	Country	4	23·5
United States	3,552	State	50	70·0
France	213	Department	90	2·4
W. Germany	96	Land	10	9·6
E. Germany	42	Bezirk	14	3·0
Netherlands	12	Province	11	1·1
Sweden	174	County (Län)	24	7·3
Switzerland	16	Canton	22	0·7

In all cases only a minimum of information is broken down by areas, and national totals still remain of paramount interest. Most yearbooks attempt to provide comparable figures for past years, either in short runs or at selected dates and in some cases separate volumes have been published dealing solely with this historical aspect of national statistics. Examples are *Annuaire Statistique de la France, Retrospectif*, I.N.S.E.E., Paris, 1961; *Union Statistics for Fifty Years*, Bureau of Census and Statistics, Pretoria, 1960, and *Historical Statistics of the United States, Colonial Times to 1957*, Bureau of the Census, Washington, D.C. The last-named volume in particular contains also a most useful text specifying sources of data, reliability, history of the statistics and much other allied information.

Unexpected windfalls in some yearbooks are an element of bilinguality (e.g. the Dutch and Swedish publications have table headings and footnotes in English) and an 'International Section' giving information similar to that in the *United Nations Statistical Yearbook*, though much reduced in volume. Especially useful in this respect is the French *Retrospectif* volume which provides an unexpected and convenient source for historical aspects of major world production.

As we have seen, national yearbooks go only part of the way towards covering the 'where?' element of distribution. Figures for even smaller areas must usually be obtained from national censuses which are too complex and varied to be described here. Alternatively, an answer, complete or partial, may often be found in map form via one of the increasing number of atlases illustrating either world production or dealing with one particular country only. As with yearbooks, these atlases have much in common; contents are very similar and there is usually an accompanying text (including some actual statistical information) of varied length and quality. Unfortunately, actual statistics are rarely specified on the maps themselves and, as has been mentioned in Chapter 1, the impossibility in many cases of 'reading back' to the figures greatly reduces the usefulness of such atlases. Unlike yearbooks, national atlases are expensive publications, not widely stocked nor published annually so that they soon become considerably out of date. Details of most national atlases in print today will be found in the periodic 'Map Bulletins' issued by Messrs. Edward Stanford Ltd., 12-14 Long Acre, London, W.C. 2, and the list below confines itself to ordinary commercially produced atlases which are more widely available.

N. Ginsburg, 'Atlas of Economic Development', Chicago, 1961.
J. Humlum, 'Atlas of Economic Geography', London, 1955.
G. Kish, 'Economic Atlas of the Soviet Union', Ann Arbor, 1960.
'Oxford Economic Atlas of the World' (2nd Edn.), Oxford, 1959.
'Oxford Regional Economic Atlas—The Middle East and North Africa', Oxford, 1959.
'Oxford Regional Economic Atlas—U.S.S.R. and Eastern Europe', Oxford, 1956.
W. Van Royen, 'The Agricultural Resources of the World, Vol. 1', New York, 1954.

SOURCES OF BRITISH STATISTICS

The relatively brief description of sources of British statistics which follows must be examined in the light of the introduction already offered at the beginning of this chapter. Generally speaking, in already-published material it is the 'Where?' aspects which have been most neglected rather than the 'How much and how many?' and so far as this latter side is concerned several important sources already exist and should be consulted wherever possible. Of these the most comprehensive and general works are E. Devons, *An Introduction to British Economic Statistics*, Cambridge, 1956, and the two-volume work published by the Royal Statistical Society entitled *The Sources and Nature of the Statistics of the United Kingdom*, London, 1952 and 1957. Extremely useful and inexpensive are the six booklets in the *Guides to Official Sources* series, prepared by the Interdepartmental Committee on Social and Economic Research and issued by H.M.S.O., London. These usually cover in detail statistics relating to the work of one particular Government Department (in brackets below), though there is cross-referencing to related material published by other Departments. The complete list, to date, is as follows:

No. 1 (1950) Labour Statistics (Ministry of Labour—employment, unemployment, wages, earnings, hours, industrial relations).
No. 2 (1951) Census Reports of Great Britain, 1801-1931.
No. 3 (1953) Local Government Statistics (Ministry of Housing and Local Government—rates, housing, water and sewerage).
No. 4 (1958) Agriculture and Food Statistics (Ministry of Agriculture, Fisheries and Food).
No. 5 (1960) Social Security Statistics (Ministry of Pensions and National Insurance and the National Assistance Board).
No. 6 (1961) Census of Production Reports.

The fullest and longest established of all the sources of British statistics is, of course, the Census, and an account of its contents will form a framework for much of the remainder of this section, supplemented by references to other sources which are relevant to a particular topic. A review of some of the more general aspects of the Census will precede more detailed description of the various parts, but in any extensive work using Census volumes the 'Guide to Official Sources, No. 2' mentioned above should be consulted; it is invaluable and may save hours of fruitless labour.

With the exception of 1941 the British Census has been taken at ten-yearly intervals since 1801 by means of questionnaires completed by householders and returned to the Registrar-General for co-ordination and condensation. Because of the personal nature of much of their contents the actual questionnaires are only released for research work after a hundred years has elapsed, so that for the Censuses of 1871 and after only the published information is available. Although no more than a fraction of the information received can actually be published, the result is a bulky and multi-volume production; thus the Census for 1871 occupied eight volumes, that for 1911 seventeen and that for 1951 well over fifty so that it is essential, for library work, to know which volume or volumes one actually requires. Unfortunately, no consistent arrangement of material has been followed, though variations on three themes can be observed. These are:

(1) Presenting all the information on *one topic* for the whole country in a single volume.
(2) Presenting all the information on all topics for *one county* in a single volume.
(3) Presenting *most* of the information for one county in one volume, but omitting certain topics which are covered by volumes relating to the whole country.

The last-mentioned method is the one now in use. Since 1861 the Census of Scotland has been separate from, though coincidental with that for England and Wales, and the Isle of Man and the Channel Islands have had separate volumes since 1881. Greater detail of the form of publication will be found in the Appendix to this book which lists all the volumes issued in the various censuses, up to 1931.

Publication of the results of the Census, which has hitherto been a somewhat protracted process, begins with a Preliminary Report, a most useful volume which includes an outline of essential information such as the population of each Local Authority and comparable figures for the previous census with the difference expressed as a percentage change. This has the advantage of presenting the most frequently sought-after information without a troublesome time-lag[1] and within one volume covering the whole country.

At first sight the Census appears to offer the possibility of obtaining comparable information on many topics over extended periods during the last 150 years, but in practice this proves to be very difficult to achieve. Census information is often not directly comparable with that obtained ten years before, for a variety of reasons among which may be listed:

(1) The increasing scope of the Census. Some topics are of only recent inclusion, e.g. workplace (journey to work), which appeared first in 1921, was omitted in 1931 and re-included in 1951.

(2) Changes in the nature of the subject, e.g. the number of employed persons which is affected by variations in school-leaving age.

[1] To date (September 1962) the only published material from the 1961 Census is the *Preliminary Reports for England & Wales and Scotland*. Publication of the remainder is, however, expected to be much speedier than in the past because of improved mechanical techniques for analysing material.

(3) Changes in definition, e.g. what constitutes a house or dwelling.

(4) Changes in the *type* of areas for which information is given.

(5) Changes in the *boundaries* of areas for which information is given. To these one might add changes in the amount and detail of information given for certain areas. Not all areas are presented in the same detail. Rural Districts are only subdivided into parishes for totals of population and houses; towns of over 50,000 population have more detailed information than others, whilst 5,000 population also forms a minor distinguishing point, more important in the past than today. Change in status, e.g. from rural parish to Urban District, will affect the amount of information available, and it is well to check the practicability of abstracting a long run of figures before starting to do so. Full details of most of the kinds of change described above are usually included in the introduction to the relevant Census volumes, but those listed under (4) and (5) may need some elaboration.

Today the modern administrative structure of counties, county boroughs and county districts (Municipal Boroughs, Urban and Rural Districts) underlies the presentation of information throughout the Census,[1] but since this hierarchy was essentially evolved only in the late nineteenth century, early censuses show, instead, figures for a bewildering variety of areas such as Ancient Counties, wapentakes, townships, etc. Fig. 48 shows the evolution of the modern system from the ancient units and should assist in using the early volumes and in assessing comparability of statistics relating to different types of area. Unfortunately, the diagram can show changes *in general terms only*, since despite the attentions of Parliament anomalies and exceptions survive to defeat the establishment of a uniform system of Local Government units. Thus two Acts of Parliament still left unscathed in 1931 fourteen of the oddities known as extra-parochial places, and even in 1951 the Census was bound to admit that Lundy Island 'appears to be extra-parochial' or, of York Castle that 'its exact status is uncertain'; these we can regard as examples of a much-reduced host of anomalous units or 'illogical' areas which in the nineteenth century made such a complex tangle of boundaries in Britain.

To modern eyes two important characteristics differentiate the arrangement of the old units from that of the new. In the first place the old units were often not physical entities, but had many detached parts of all sizes often many miles from the parent area; secondly, each large unit rarely contained a *whole number* of small units. Examples of the first type survive in the well-known detached parts of Worcestershire and Flintshire, but this will scarcely prepare the uninitiated for parishes in twenty or more separate parts, or for a former detached portion of County Durham at Crayke, near York, quite twenty-five miles beyond the county boundary. Many of these 'parts' were removed under Acts of 1844 (counties) and 1882 (parishes) and fortunately in the latter case, where they were most numerous, they were often of land only, without population.

On the whole the second characteristic is more troublesome statistically. Apart from hundreds and wapentakes, which always seem to have fitted exactly into counties, there was no self-contingency of smaller units within the larger ones. Thus townships ran into two parishes, parishes ran into two counties, as also did Urban and Rural Sanitary Districts and

---

[1] Figures for other areas, e.g. ecclesiastical parishes, are given, but the general arrangement is made under headings relating to contemporary Local Authorities.

particularly Poor Law Unions (Stamford Union extended into *five* counties), a state of affairs which was responsible for many of the differences between the ancient counties and the new administrative ones when these were created. The Local Government Act of 1894 had the last word on this subject, declaring that 'no Civil Parish could be partly in an Urban and partly in a Rural District or in two Administrative Counties'.

Another term appearing in Fig. 48 and also likely to cause confusion is the word 'parish', which even today retains a dual meaning, 'ecclesiastical' often being implied in common

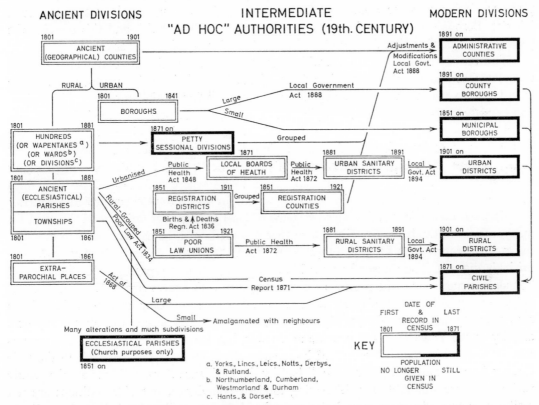

Fig. 48. Relationship of Ancient and Modern Administrative Areas in England and Wales and their Occurrence in Census Reports.

usage, but 'civil' in most official documents. Originally of ecclesiastical origin and referring broadly to the area attached to a particular church, it maintained a parallel existence with the ancient unit of local territorial organisation in Saxon England—namely, the *township* (i.e. a settlement and the lands belonging to it). So long as each village had its own church the two areas would frequently coincide, and where this happened the term 'parish' tended to supplant the older one, as in much of southern England where parish and township once coincided. In the poorer northern counties, however, churches were fewer and *several* townships frequently formed a *single* parish, giving the appearance of a two-tier structure, though matters were not always so simple as this. There was the usual overlapping of boundaries, e.g. in the West Riding Cumberworth Half township extended into three parishes and two wapentakes, and there were also extra-parochial places, neither townships nor parishes and which had a strange variety of origins.

Enough has been said to show that throughout Britain under this system the smallest local units had neither common terminology nor common status and, therefore, in the Census Report of 1871 the term 'Civil Parish' was introduced to define the local unit of territorial organisation. The old 'simple' or undivided ecclesiastical parish became a civil parish, but so also did the old townships in 'compound' parishes and many of the old extra-parochial places too if they were large enough.[1] Rather confusingly each larger unit such as an Urban District, Borough or County Borough was also made a Civil Parish and this remains the general rule today[2] so that the term 'Civil Parish' applies to units of all sizes.

The various Acts of Parliament which attempted to rationalise the boundaries of these *Civil* Parishes had no powers to alter those of the old *ecclesiastical* parishes, and the two units began to exist separately, side by side, but often relating to different areas. The separation persists to the present day, complicated by much subdivision of ecclesiastical parishes in urban areas, as new churches were built, and amalgamation in rural areas. Figures for the populations of ecclesiastical parishes are included in Census Reports but are little used, largely because there is no published map of ecclesiastical parish boundaries. This is rather unfortunate, especially in some cities and large towns where ecclesiastical parishes form smaller and often more 'local' units than the 'wards' for which the Census provides figures.[3]

Between the ancient and modern systems of local government units stood the need for many, often drastic, boundary changes so that it sometimes becomes necessary to establish the exact extent of areas for which figures are given at different dates. This may prove surprisingly difficult. The Census Reports have always given, in a separate table, details of all boundary changes since the previous Census, together with figures (for population and area only) to allow adjustment of either total to the other area, but they have never included a map showing the *extent* of these changes. For local boundary changes of almost any date enquiry at the Town Hall will provide an answer, but for areas further afield two sources may be used. The 'official' record of boundaries of all kinds is the half-inch to the mile County Administrative Diagrams, published by the Ordnance Survey. These are frequently revised and are admirable for delineating modern boundaries, but older editions are not easily come by and former boundaries can often be more easily traced from the ordinary Ordnance Survey topographical maps. Of these the 1:2500 (25 in. to the mile) is the map par excellence for boundaries, which are recorded in great detail; the 6-in. map likewise shows very complete information but these large scales make it difficult to gain access to cover for extensive areas. Fortunately, all editions of the 1-in. map except the 'Popular' (or 4th Edition), current from 1920 to about 1939, have recorded parish boundaries, and since

[1] By an Act of 1868. Small ones were supposed to be amalgamated with their neighbours, but quite a few 'escaped' (see above).

[2] In a few exceptional cases *several* civil parishes will be found within a larger unit, e.g. Malvern U.D. (Worcs.) contains 4 civil parishes; Much Wenlock M.B. (Salop.) 9, and the County Borough of Kingston-upon-Hull 2.

[3] *Crockford's Clerical Directory* conveniently records the population of all ecclesiastical parishes (at the date of the last census).

copies of old editions are often found in libraries or second-hand, these offer the most readily accessible solution to the problem. The parishes shown are usually 'ancient' (ecclesiastical) ones until about 1880, but civil parishes after that date; the approximate periods during which the various editions were current in England and Wales are listed below.

Edition	Current
1st 'Old Series'	1801 (south)–1870 (north)
2nd 'New Series'	1870–1885
3rd 'Small Sheet Series'	1885–1920
3rd 'Large Sheet Series'	1905–1920
5th	1930–1939 (south of about Birmingham only)

Despite the number and variety of these transforming boundary changes their main trends can be summarised fairly easily. In the late nineteenth century new urban and rural units had been created, either by adapting ancient ones or by carving out areas quite unrelated to older boundaries; the whole range had been 'tidied up' and the modern units had emerged in embryo by 1894. Since then five main types of change have occurred, namely:

(1) Piecemeal extensions to growing towns and cities.
(2) Amalgamations of many rural parishes.
(3) Amalgamations of many small urban districts.
(4) Creation of some new urban districts.
(5) Reorganisation of the *grouping* of units in rural areas into new Rural Districts.

Following the passing of the Local Government Act, 1929, particularly widespread and drastic boundary changes occurred, so much so that the 1931 Census, which described the areas before revision, had to be augmented by special tables (Part II of each County Volume) recording at least the population and area of each of the newly constituted authorities. Fig. 49 illustrates an area where particularly marked changes separate the ancient and modern boundaries and helps to give some idea of the difficulties which may arise from this source. The operations of the present Boundary Commission, when concluded, seem likely to introduce another hiatus into the areas traditionally used for Census purposes in Britain.

Having introduced the census in general terms we are now in a position to review some of the main topics it describes and add further sources of information.

POPULATION

A recording of the total population of various areas has always formed a primary aim of the Census; it is unfortunate that, obtained in this manner, statistics only become available every ten years. Populations recorded are *de facto* and not *de jure*, i.e. the population *actually present* on census night and not the population which *ought to have been or would normally have been present*. The difference is usually small (see, for example, Census of England and Wales, 1951, *Usual Residence and Workplace* volume), but can occasionally be troublesome. The unusual example of Leyburn has already been seen in Chapter 6, and the following two footnotes to the 1911 Census will emphasise the point:

KSM

146

Fig. 49. Upper Calder Valley (West Yorkshire)—Administrative areas before and after evolution of 'modern' units in the late nineteenth century. Note the carving-out of valley-centred urban units (Todmorden M.B.; Hebden Bridge U.D.; Mytholmroyd U.D.; Luddendenfoot U.D. and Sowerby Bridge U.D.) from old plateau-centred townships. Changes made in the 1930's confused the position even more. Hebden Bridge U.D. and Mytholmroyd U.D. amalgamated to form Hebden Royd U.D.; Sowerby Bridge U.D., Luddendenfoot U.D., Norland parish and part of Midgley U.D. (the rest went to Wadsworth parish) became Sowerby Bridge U.D. and Soyland U.D. and Barkisland U.D. became part of Ripponden U.D. *Source:* O.S. Maps, 6 in. Yorkshire (1st Edition 1850) and 1 in. (2nd Edition 1910)

'The population in 1911 of Lyme Regis Civil Parish includes 473 persons on board H.M. Ships.'

'The large increase in the population of Lancing Civil Parish is attributed mainly to the presence of students and staff of Lancing College, which was closed for the Easter vacation at the Census of 1901.'

The most troublesome discrepancies of this kind usually have their origins in variation in 'institutional population', which may be considerable (e.g. in 1931 over 7% of the population of Gosforth U.D. (Northumberland) were in institutions for the insane or mentally deficient), and the best means of avoiding mistakes from this source is to use the figures for the population 'in private households', already referred to in Chapter 6.

Intercensal change receives considerable attention in Census Reports. Comparable figures for the same area at the previous census are provided and the change is usually recorded as a percentage and also subdivided into components of natural increase and migration.

For statistics of population at dates between censuses, only estimates are available, the fullest account being contained in the *Registrar-General's Statistical Review of England and Wales*[1] which records not only estimated population for local authority areas but also such features as births, deaths, birth rates, death rates, marriages, and local government elections. Publication is normally in three volumes, Part I, Medical (relating mainly to mortality), Part II, Population, and Part III, Commentary.

Among the considerable amount of information on other aspects of population found in the Census Reports are tables covering age and sex distribution among local populations,[2] social class of occupied males, marital condition and birthplace, as well as details of the possession of various household arrangements such as number of rooms, piped water or a bath.

Among statistical sources censuses are unusual in that they are able to answer not only 'How much or how many', but also to go a considerable way towards providing the answer to 'Where?' as well. For more precise information on the location of population the best source is the annual *Register of Electors* which provides, for each parish or polling district the names *and addresses* of all adults entitled to vote at elections. As such it can be used to establish a very detailed distribution of the *adult* population, but unfortunately no easy way exists of extending this to cover *total* population. The usual practice is to obtain an estimate of total population in the area covered by the register and allot a proportional number of children to each adult; this is often reasonably accurate for large blocks of adult population but cannot be expected to work too well for small groups. Copies of the Register can be obtained at a small fee from the appropriate Electoral Registration Officer (usually the Clerk to the County or County Borough Council) who is also responsible for retaining previous Registers, from which historical comparisons can be made and changes determined.

[1] Published by H.M.S.O., London, as are all Government publications referred to in this chapter unless otherwise specified. There is a companion volume for Scotland.

[2] The author very regretfully concludes that he can find no foundation for the statement, which appeared in a recently published humorous article, that these volumes include a table headed 'Population of Great Britain, broken down by age and sex'.

INDUSTRY AND OCCUPATION

A second great preoccupation of the Census has been to establish some account of the occupations of the population. The problem has proved enormously complicated and early results in particular were not very successful or reliable. The great difficulty was to establish a suitable classification so that people who described themselves as 'sad iron grinders' (engineering), 'bottom knockers' (pottery), 'banknote finishers' (printing) or 'twisters' (many industries), along with thousands of other categories could somehow be accommodated within a classification of manageable proportions. At first a relatively small number of extremely broad groups was used, but from 1851 onwards there began to evolve the classification of occupations by classes and sub-classes, later called orders and sub-orders, which has been maintained with constant modifications to the present day.

Occupational statistics, it should be stressed, relate to the *kind of work a person does, irrespective of the industry which employs him*, and the twenty-seven main orders contain therefore such groups as 'clerks and typists', 'painters and decorators', 'warehousemen' and 'workers in unskilled occupations', many of whom can and often do move about from one industry to another. In this respect they should be carefully distinguished from a second set of figures, the '*Industry* Tables' which have appeared in the Census since 1921 and in which a worker is classified by the *industry which employs him, irrespective of what job he does*. The distinction needs watching, particularly since many of the headings used in the two tables are not greatly different from one another at first sight. Nevertheless, the distinction is quite clear cut. So far as the Occupation Tables go a lorry driver, for example, falls unambiguously into Order XVII, 'Persons employed in Transport and Communications'; from the Industrial Table's point of view he might be allocated to any one of the main industrial groups, to 'Transport and Communications', to 'Distributive Trades' and so on, according to the main business of his employer. The more 'industrial' terms in the Occupation Tables usually refer only to workers actually making the product of the industry and not to ancillary staff such as office workers, managers, cleaners, etc., so that the total for a particular industry in the Industry Tables will usually be considerably larger than that for the most comparable heading in the Occupation Tables.

One more distinction must be made. 'Occupation' is a *personal* characteristic and the tables have therefore always been arranged to show what *occupations the people of X follow, no matter where these take place*. The Industry Tables for 1931 followed a similar arrangement and show *the industries which occupied the people of X no matter where they were*. This was different from both 1921 and 1951 where the Industry tables had a *place* type of arrangement showing totals for *the numbers employed in the industries in X no matter where the workers came from*, so that comparisons with the 1931 figures cannot be made. The most striking example of the differences involved comes from the figures for the City of London shown below:

	Census of		
	1921	*1931*	*1951*
Occupation Tables, total occupied	8,996	7,390*	3,591
Industry Tables, total employed	†	6,978*	337,486

* Theoretically these two figures should be the same; the reasons for the difference are not given.
† Separate figures were not provided for units with small populations at the 1921 Census.

The table for Wigan (Lancashire), on p. 150, illustrates the kind of differences which can occur in a medium-sized town. Note, for example, that the Industry Tables 'play down' the role of mining, simply because most of Wigan's miners work at collieries outside the Borough Boundary (1951 being a *place* and not a *personal* year for Industry Tables).

As with population this decennial census information often needs supplementing in between censuses, but it is difficult to get anything approaching the detailed *local* figures which the Census gives. Regular figures on manpower, and such other topics as unemployment, short time and overtime and labour turnover are collected by the Ministry of Labour and published in the *Ministry of Labour Gazette*, issued monthly. Totals are usually for the whole country, subdivided by industry in the same manner as the Census Industry Tables;[1] the only local figures given are for unemployment (each month), but even these relate to Employment Exchange Areas which do not coincide with, or often even approximate to, the Local Authority Areas used for Census purposes. The annual exchange of Employment Cards at each Employment Exchange makes it possible, once a year, to establish the way in which workers registered at that exchange are subdivided amongst the various industries. Unfortunately, these figures are not published, but from the frequency with which they appear in theses, town planning analyses, etc., it would appear that they are often disclosed to *bona fide* research workers.

For some industries local information may be obtained from a yearbook or similar sources, some of which are excellent, e.g. the *Colliery Year Book and Coal Trades Directory* which lists men employed above and below ground and annual production at each colliery in Britain and many in Western Europe and the U.S.A.;[2] in addition most of the nationalised industries and organisations publish an 'Annual Report' or similarly titled volume dealing with their activities and containing varying amounts of statistics.

Unlike the Census, yearbooks often assess industry from a *production* rather than a *manpower* point of view and for wider information of this kind quite a different set of official sources can be consulted. The fullest of these are the Censuses of Production which have been taken by the Board of Trade in 1907, 1912, 1924, 1930, 1935, 1946 (partial), 1948 and in various forms yearly since then, although more fully at three-yearly intervals from 1948. As well as details of production both by quantity and value the censuses have recorded employment, number and size of establishments, costs, investment, fuel and power equipment, analysed mainly by industries for the whole of Great Britain, but with a very limited breakdown into smaller units such as countries and Standard Regions.[3] Publication is in multi-volume form, a 'notes and summary volume' plus several sections devoted to groups of the various industries covered by the census, i.e. broadly those in orders II to XVII of the

[1] Following the drawing up of a Standard Industrial Classification in 1948 the same subdivisions have been used, where applicable, in the Industry Tables of the Census and for figures prepared by the Ministry of Labour and the Board of Trade.

[2] The *Municipal Yearbook* is another useful source of statistics relating to Local Authority activities of all kinds.

[3] The Standard Regions have been widely used in post-war official statistical publications where a breakdown of the country into medium-sized areas is required. Eleven in number their boundaries are indicated in Fig. 34 and they will be found further defined in the Industry or Occupations Volumes of the 1951 Census. The same applies to the Standard Conurbations, which date from the 1951 Census.

WIGAN (LANCS.) CENSUS, 1951

Occupational Tables				*Industry Tables*	
Total occupied persons	41,351	35,255	Total employed, all industries		
Order				*Order*	
I	Fishermen	1			
II	Agricultural, etc., Occupations	230	110	Agriculture, Forestry, Fishing	I
III	Mining and Quarrying Occupations	5,194	438	Mining and Quarrying	II
IV	Workers in Glass, Ceramics, Cement, etc.	72	123	Ceramics, Glass, Cement	III
V	Coal Gas Makers, Workers in Chemicals	328	421	Chemicals and Allied Trades	IV
			167	Metal Manufacture	V
VI	Workers in Metal Manufacture, Engineering	3,815	2,387	Engineering, Shipbuilding, Electrical Goods	VI
			585	Vehicles	VII
			759	Metal Goods (n.e.s.*)	VIII
			39	Precision Instruments and Jewellery	IX
VII	Textile Workers	4,055	6,368	Textiles	X
VIII	Leather Workers, Fur Dressers	448	163	Leather Goods and Fur	XI
IX	Makers of Textile Goods and articles of Dress	2,301	3,333	Clothing	XII
X	Makers of Food, Drink and Tobacco	543	986	Food, Drink, Tobacco	XIII
XI	Workers in Wood, Cane or Cork	966	692	Manufacture of Wood and Cork	XIV
XII	Workers in Paper, Printers	188	348	Paper and Printing	XV
XIII	Makers of Other Products	264	182	Other Manufacturing Industries	XVI
XIV	Workers in Building and Contracting	1,851	1,900	Building and Contracting	XVII
XV	Painters and Decorators	455	684	Gas, Water, Electricity	XVIII
XVI	Administrators, Directors, Managers (n.e.s.*)	467			
XVII	Persons employed in Transport	2,541	2,757	Transport and Communications	XIX
XVIII	Commercial, Finance, etc. (excl. Clerical)	4,038	5,872	Distributive Trades	XX
			655	Insurance, Banking, Finance	XXI
XIX	Professional and Technical (excl. Clerical)	1,677	2,076	Professional Services	XXII
XX	Persons employed in Defence Services	408	1,679	Public Administration and Defence	XXIII
XXI	Persons engaged in Entertainment and Sport	131			
XXII	Persons engaged in Personal Service	2,543	2,503	Miscellaneous Services	XXIV
XXIII	Clerks, Typists, etc.	2,325			
XXIV	Warehousemen, Storekeepers, Packers, etc.	869			
XXV	Stationary Engine Drivers, Stokers, etc.	541			
XXVI	Workers in Unskilled Occupations (n.e.s.*)	4,835			
XXVII	Others and Undefined	275	18	Not stated, ill-defined	
XXVIII	Retired, Not Gainfully Occupied	23,849			
	Total (equal to population aged 15 and over)	65,200			

* n.e.s. = not elsewhere specified.

Standard Industrial Classification (see Industry Tables for Wigan above), although this has varied slightly in the past.

Parallel in many ways to the Census of Production but dealing with wholesale and retail distribution and some service trades is the *Census of Distribution and Other Services, 1950*, taken by the Board of Trade. Separate volumes for wholesale and retail activities give accounts of the number of establishments, receipts, sales, employment, wages, cost of transport, etc., usually for Great Britain, but sometimes for countries, Standard Regions and Conurbations. The section on retail distribution is quite unusual in going into much smaller subdivisions than this, giving total number of establishments, sales, employees and wages for towns of over 2,500 population and subdividing these totals among a great variety of trades where population exceeds 25,000. A second similarly named census followed in 1957, but as this was based on sampling, information could be given only for Great Britain as a whole; wholesale trade was not covered in this second census.

Locating the units of industrial production or wholesale and retail distribution is, perhaps, rather easier than trying to 'tie down' the population. As a first source of information the *Classified Telephone Directory* proves most useful, whilst many trades and industries have their own yearbook or directory. Once again the Ordnance Survey maps can be a great help, the largest scale map published for the principle urban areas at 1 : 1250 (50 in. to a mile) showing the use of all buildings which are not dwelling houses, offices or shops. The 25 in. and 6 in. to the mile maps do the same at least for many of the larger units, and for big industrial premises usually give the name of the works and the industry carried on there; older editions of these maps can sometimes be used to obtain former distributions and check changes of use, but it should be noted that the names of the premises in particular are apt to change (the same applies to farms shown on O.S. maps), so that a map several years old may not be a great help in locating establishments listed by their present names. Formerly even 1 in. to the mile maps marked the nature of many sizeable isolated industrial premises, e.g. Mill (Cotton), Colliery, Mine (Barytes), and so on, but modern practice seems to be to reduce this to the much less specific 'works' or 'mine'.

AGRICULTURE

Though details of agricultural employment are recorded in the Census it is necessary, as with industry, to look elsewhere for details of production. Fortunately, quite complete information is available, arising from an annual return made each June to the Ministry of Agriculture from all holdings of more than one acre. The principal statistical results from this return are published annually by the Ministry in *Agricultural Statistics—England and Wales*.[1] Information provided includes acreage of land under a wide variety of crops, grass and rough grazings, totals of various livestock, estimated yields of crops, size of holdings and workers employed, and fortunately for a great deal of this information *county* totals are available as well as national ones. A second section on horticulture adds figures for vegetables and fruit in rather greater detail.

Local information for areas smaller than counties is not published but the Ministry are prepared to extract totals under most of the headings listed above for any particular parish

[1] There is a similar volume for Scotland.

or series of parishes. An estimate of the approximate cost[1] of this work will be provided on application to Block 'B', Agricultural Census Branch, Government Buildings, Epsom Road, Guildford, Surrey, although research workers who are able to visit Guildford are allowed, subject to prior arrangements, to extract the totals themselves, free of charge. The annual nature of the census means that runs of figures are quite easily obtained and the results from earlier censuses allow ample scope for detection of changes.

A record of the distribution of the six main types of land use in Britain is provided by the maps published at 1 in. to a mile to illustrate the Land Utilisation Survey of Britain, carried out in 1931 (England) and 1932 (Wales and Scotland). Unfortunately there was a very considerable delay in publishing many of these sheets and it should be remembered when using them that whatever the date of publication the information shown relates to the period of the survey and not later. Accompanying the maps was a report of the Survey, published in 92 parts (one for each administrative county in Britain) under the title of *The Land of Britain*, whilst a later work, L. D. Stamp *The Land of Britain, Its Use and Misuse* (third edition), London, 1962, provides a co-ordinating account of the survey generally and analyses its results. Both of these accounts, and the county volumes in particular, form excellent supplementary sources to the maps, providing an enormous amount of information on many local distributions besides those of land use. The maps show the six main categories of forest and woodland; meadowland and permanent grass; arable; heathland, moorland and rough pasture; houses with gardens, orchards and nurseries; and land agriculturally unproductive. Unfortunately, many are now out of print and those that remain, as well as the county volumes, are obtainable only through Messrs. Edward Stanford, Ltd., 12-14 Long Acre, London, W.C.2.

A similar, more ambitious project, the Second Land Utilisation Survey of Britain is at the moment in preparation under the direction of Miss Alice Coleman, M.A., King's College, London. The published maps, of which only a handful have so far appeared, are at 1 : 25,000 scale (2½ in. to 1 mile) and the material recorded is in much greater detail than on the earlier survey; several varieties of cropland are shown as well as useful information such as the type of industry carried on at the various industrial premises. A series of county reports is contemplated, but none is yet published.

These surveys apart, it is worth while remembering that most Ordnance Survey maps, even down to the one inch scale, have always differentiated important types of land use such as woodland, moorland and rough pasture, marsh, orchards and (more recently) glasshouses.

TRANSPORT AND COMMUNICATIONS

It is an unrewarding task to try to obtain details of *local* movements of people, goods or vehicles in Britain. For railways, fairly detailed information, though in units of oddly varying sizes, was formerly available in the annual 'Railway Returns',[2] but the amalgamation of the railways into four large main line companies in 1923 removed most of the local element from this source and figures became available generally only for large sprawling entities without geographical coherence. The only exceptions to this rule were the few lines which

[1] The present basis of the charge is twelve items for one shilling.
[2] Issued annually by the Ministry of Transport.

were not amalgamated (usually impecunious local oddities) or lines jointly owned or worked, for which figures continued to be provided until the Railway Returns ceased in 1938; these exceptions occasionally contain a few surprisingly useful local systems, such as the Liverpool Overhead Railway, the Mersey Railway and the Manchester South Junction and Altrincham line. Information is given on such items as capital, receipts, working expenses and traffic.

Nationalisation has not removed this general drawback of arrangement by very large regions (admittedly more geographically compact), and figures for these will be found in *Transport Statistics* issued monthly by the British Transport Commission.

Details of the number of trains using sections of railway can be obtained from the public timetables (passenger trains) or the less-well-known Working Timetables (all trains), although the latter source is not on sale to the general public.

For information on local road traffic, though not on amounts of goods or passengers carried, the position is a little better. Traffic Censuses have been taken by the Ministry of Transport since 1922, usually at three- or four-yearly intervals up to 1938 and since then in 1950 (full), 1954 (Trunk and Class I roads only) and 1961 (Trunk Roads only). Unfortunately, even where the results of these censuses have been published, the Reports deal only with general aspects and do not give figures for individual census points. Local information of this sort is usually best obtained through the appropriate Highway Authority (usually the County or County Borough Council) who in fact were responsible for obtaining the information for the Ministry on the occasion of each census.

Figures relating to road transport for the whole country will be found in *Public Road Passenger Transport in Great Britain* and *Road Motor Vehicles* (based on an annual census of licensed vehicles), both issued annually by the Ministry of Transport.

A useful account of local *personal* movements is contained in the 'Journey to Work' tables found in the '*Workplace*' volume for the 1921 national Census and the corresponding *Usual Residence and Workplace* volume in the 1951 census. Movements are classified by Local Authority areas and the data recorded form a useful basis for a study of commuting Britain.

Traffic at the various British ports, along with an enormously detailed account of British overseas trade generally will be found in the four-volume *Annual Statement of the Trade of the United Kingdom*.

In any search for sources of statistical information on all aspects of life in Britain government publications must of necessity provide the majority of the results. As all library users will know, few types of publication are apt to cause so much trouble in indexing or in obtaining particular titles and 'authorship'; for obtaining specific information of this sort as well as a comprehensive account of publications of all kinds works such as *Catalogue of Parliamentary Papers, 1801-1900*; *General Index to Parliamentary Papers, 1900-1949* and the annual *Catalogue of Government Publications* will be found invaluable.

APPENDIX

LIST OF CENSUS REPORTS FOR GREAT BRITAIN, 1801–1931

Reports	Year of Publication	Order Paper ( ) or Command [ ] No.
1801. GREAT BRITAIN		
Abstracts of the Answers and Returns:		
Enumeration. Part I England: Part II Scotland ...	1801, 1802	(140, 9, 112)
Parish Registers	1801	—
1811. GREAT BRITAIN		
Comparative Statement of Population etc., Gt. Britain, 1801, 1811.	1812	(12)
Abstracts of the Answers and Returns:		
Preliminary Observations		
Enumeration Abstract	1812	(316, 317)
Parish-Register Abstract		
1821. GREAT BRITAIN		
Comparative Statement of Population etc., Gt. Britain, 1801, 1811, 1821.	1822	(8)
Abstracts of the Answers and Returns:		
Preliminary Observations		
Enumeration Abstract	1822	(502)
Parish-Register Abstract		
1831. GREAT BRITAIN		
Comparative Account of the Population of Great Britain, 1801, 1811, 1821, 1831.	1831	(348)
Abstracts of the Answers and Returns:		
Enumeration. Vols. I & II with Index to the Names of Places at the end of Vol. II.	1833	(149, Appendix 612)
Parish Registers	1833	—
1841. GREAT BRITAIN		
Statements on Population[1]	1841	(52)

[1] The full title is '*Accounts of the Total Population 1841, of each county of Gt. Britain; distinguishing males and females and showing the rate per cent. increase or decrease in each county compared with population 1831; also the number of houses inhabited, uninhabited and building according to the Census, 1841; similar returns for Channel Islands, Isle of Man; also, comparative statements of the population and number of houses, 1801, 1811, 1821, 1831, for each county in Gt. Britain; also population of each city and Royal and Parliamentary Burgh in Scotland*'.

Reports	Year of Publication	Command No.
Abstracts of the Answers and Returns:		
Enumeration. Part I England and Wales: Part II Scotland with Index to Names of Places at end of each Part.	1843	(496)
Index to Names of Places, England and Wales	1843	(511)
Index to Names of Places, Scotland	1843	(498, 506)
Age. Part I England and Wales: Part II Scotland ...	1843	(497)
Occupations. Part I England and Wales: Part II Scotland	1844	(587–588)
Parish Registers	1845	—
Introductory Remarks to the Census Abstracts (Reprinted as a separate volume)	1844	—
1851. GREAT BRITAIN		
Forms and instructions for the use of persons employed in taking an account of the population of Gt. Britain.	1851	[1339]
Tables of Population and Houses	1851	[1399]
Population Tables I. Vols. I & II. Numbers of Inhabitants.	1852	[1631, 1632]
Population Tables II. Vols. I & II. Ages, Civil Conditions, Occupations and Birthplaces.	1854	[1691, I-II]
Index to Names of Places in the Population Tables ...	1852	[1633]
Religious Worship. England and Wales	1853	[1690]
Education. England and Wales	1854	[1692]
Religious Worship and Education. Scotland	1854	[1764]
1861. ENGLAND AND WALES		
Tables of Population and Houses	1861	[2846]
Reports:		
Population Tables. Number and Distribution of the People (Vol. I).	1862	[3056]
Population Tables. Ages, Civil Condition, Occupations and Birthplaces (Vol. II).	1863	[3221]
General Report (Vol. III)	1863	[3221]
1861. SCOTLAND		
Tables of Population, etc.	1861	[2870]
Population Tables and Report:		
Vol. I. Population of various types of areas, Houses ...	1862	[3013]
Vol. II. Ages, Civil Condition, Occupations, Birthplaces.	1864	[3275]
1871. ENGLAND AND WALES		
Preliminary Report and Tables of Population and Houses ...	1871	c. 381
Population Tables:		
Vol. I. Ancient Counties	1872	c. 676

Reports	Year of Publication	Command No.
Vol. II. Registration or Union Counties, with Index to Names of Places in Population Tables. ...	1872	c. 676–1
Population Abstracts:		
Vol. III. Ages, Civil Condition, Occupations and Birthplaces.	1873	c. 872
General Report	1873	c. 872–1
1871. SCOTLAND		
Tables of Population, etc.	1871	c. 380
Population of Scotland with Report:		
Vol. I. Population of various types of areas, Houses ...	1872	c. 592
Vol. II. Ages, Education, Civil Conditions, Birthplaces, Occupations.	1874	c. 841
1881. ENGLAND AND WALES		
Preliminary Report	1881	c. 2955
Tables:		
Area, Houses and Population in Ancient Counties (Vol. I).	1883	c. 3562
Area, Houses and Population in Registration Counties (Vol. II).	1883	c. 3563
Ages, Marital Condition, Occupations and Birthplaces (Vol. III).	1883	c. 3722
Islands in the British Seas (Vol. IV)	1883	c. 3643
General Report	1883	c. 3797
1881. SCOTLAND		
Tables of Population, etc.	1881	c. 2957
Population of Scotland with Report:		
Vol. I. Population of various types of areas, public institutions	1882	c. 3320
Vol. II. Ages, Education, Civil Condition, Birthplaces, Occupations, General Index.	1883	c. 3657
1891. ENGLAND AND WALES		
Preliminary Report	1891	c. 6422
Area, Housing and Population:		
Administrative and Ancient Counties (Vol. I) ...	1893	c. 6948
Registration Area and Sanitary Districts (Vol. II) ...	1893	c. 6948–1
Ages, Marital Condition, Occupations, Birthplaces and Infirmities (Vol. III).	1893	c. 7058
General Report (Vol. IV)	1893	c. 7222
Islands in the British Seas	1893	c. 7133
Index to Population Tables	1893	c. 7216

Reports	Year of Publication	Command No.
1891. SCOTLAND		
Tables of Population, etc.	1891	c. 6390
Population of Scotland with Report:		
Vol. I. Report with Appendices, Population of various types of areas, Houses.	1892	c. 6755
Supplement to Vol. I.	1893	c. 6936
Vol. II. Ages, Education, Civil Condition, Birthplaces, place, Occupations, Working Status, Indices.	1893	c. 6937, c. 7134
1901. ENGLAND AND WALES		
Preliminary Report	1901	Cd. 616
Series of County Parts	1902–3	—
Index to Population Tables in the County volumes ...	1903	Cd. 1826
Islands in the British Seas	1903	Cd. 1473
Summary Tables	1903	Cd. 1523
General Report, with Appendices	1904	Cd. 2174
1901. SCOTLAND		
Preliminary Report	1901	Cd. 644
Parliamentary Burghs, Counties, Population, etc., 1901 *and* 1891	1902	Cd. 898
Population of Scotland with Report:		
Vol. I. Population of various types of areas, Houses ...	1902	Cd. 1257
Vol. II. Ages, Marital Condition, Education and Birth-places	1903	Cd. 1481
Vol. III. Report, Occupations	1903	Cd. 1798
1911. ENGLAND AND WALES		
Preliminary Report[1]	1911	Cd. 5705
Area, Families and Population:		
Administrative Areas (Vol. I)	1912	Cd. 6258
Registration Areas (Vol. II)	1912	Cd. 6259
Parliamentary Areas (Vol. III)	1912	Cd. 6343
Ecclesiastical Areas (Vol. IV)	1912	Cd. 6360
Index to Population Tables Vols. I-IV (Vol. V)	1913	Cd. 6576
Buildings of various kinds (Vol. VI)	1913	Cd. 6577
Ages and Condition as to Marriage (Vol. VII)	1913	Cd. 6610
Tenements (Vol. VIII)	1913	Cd. 6910
Birthplaces (Vol. IX)	1913	Cd. 7017

[1] This publication also included preliminary reports for Scotland, Ireland, Isle of Man and Channel Islands.

Reports	Year of Publication	Command No.
Occupations and Industries, Parts I & II	1913–14	Cd. 7018, 7019
Appendix. Classification of Occupations and Rules adopted for such a Classification (Vol. X)	1915	Cd. 7660
Infirmities (Vol. XI)	1913	Cd. 7020
Languages spoken in Wales and Monmouthshire (Vol. XII)	1913	Cd. 6911
Fertility of Marriage Parts I & II (Vol. XIII)	1917 & 1923	Cd. 8678
Islands in the British Seas	1913	Cd. 6922
Summary Tables	1915	Cd. 7929
General Report with Appendices	1917	Cd. 8491
1911. SCOTLAND		
Preliminary Report	1911	Cd. 5700
Reports and Tables:		
Vol. I. City and and County Parts	1912	Cd. 6907 to Cd. 6907—XXXVI
Vol. II. Population, Ages and Conjugal Condition, Occupations, Birthplaces, Housing, Gaelic-speaking	1913	Cd. 6896
Vol. III. Occupations by birthplace, Nationalities, Infirmities, Fertility	1913	Cd. 9163
1921. ENGLAND AND WALES		
Preliminary Report	1921	Cmd. 1485
Series of County Parts	1923–4	—
Workplaces in London and Five Home Counties	1923	—
Workplaces	1925	—
Ecclesiastical Areas	1924	—
Classification of Occupations	1924	—
Occupation Tables	1924	—
Classification of Industries	1924	—
Industry Tables	1925	—
Dependency, Orphanhood and Fertility	1925	—
Isle of Man	1924	—
Channel Islands	1924	—
Index to Names of Places	1924	—
General Tables	1925	—
General Report with Appendices	1927	—
1921. SCOTLAND		
Preliminary Report	1921	Cmd. 1473
Reports and Tables:		
Vol. I. City and County Parts	1922–4	—
Vol. II. Population, Ages, Conjugal Condition, Orphanhood, Birthplaces, Gaelic-speaking, Housing ...	1923	—
Vol. III. Occupations and Industries	1924	—
Vol. IV. Dependent Children	1924	—

Reports	Year of Publication	Command No.
1931. ENGLAND AND WALES		
Preliminary Report	1931	—
Series of County Parts, I and II	1932–40	—
Ecclesiastical Areas	1933	—
Classification of Occupations	1934	—
Occupation Tables	1934	—
Classification of Industries	1934	—
Industry Tables	1934	—
Housing	1935	—
Isle of Man	1933	—
Channel Islands	1933	—
General Tables	1935	—
General Report	1950	—
1931. SCOTLAND		
Preliminary Report	1931	—
Reports and Tables:		
Vol. I. City and County Parts	1932	—
Vol. II. Population, Ages, Conjugal Conditions, Birthplaces, Gaelic-speaking and Housing	1933	—
Vol. III. Occupations and Industries	1934	—

General Index

(Numbers in heavy type refer to illustrations)

Index of Places Referred to in the Text or Diagrams

(British entries are treated individually; all others are listed by countries)